THE
ROYAL SOCIETY OF
EDINBURGH
(1783–1983)

SOCIETAS REGALIS EDINBURGI

THE
ROYAL SOCIETY OF
EDINBURGH
(1783–1983)

THE FIRST TWO HUNDRED YEARS

By
Neil Campbell
and
R. Martin S. Smellie

With a Foreword by The Hon. Lord Cameron

The Royal Society of Edinburgh
22, 24 George Street
Edinburgh   EH2 2PQ

1983

Printed in Great Britain
by Latimer Trend & Company Ltd, Plymouth

Foreword

The Society now approaches completion of 200 years of life and embarkation on its third century, one which, it is plain to see, will present for solution problems economic, social, political, and scientific, not only different in degree from those which faced our predecessors in the last two centuries of our Society's life, but different in quality, substance and magnitude alike. It is therefore peculiarly fitting at this point in our history to take stock of the past in preparation and encouragement for the future. The record of the past lies in the chapters of this necessarily compressed narrative of the origins and purpose of the Society and of the careers and personal contributions of some of its most notable and distinguished—the two not necessarily co-terminous—Fellows and Officers. The function of such a publication as this is not to serve as a definitive and detailed record of the achievements and constitutional history of the Society or of the personal records of its Fellows, but to survey the past, to recall the Society's origins and to place it in the context of the life of Scotland as a whole and of the wider world of science and learning. In this the reader may well think the authors have succeeded admirably and far beyond the modest claims set out in their preface. But as this is a record of the past so also it is legitimate to hope it will serve as a spur for those in whose hands will lie the future of the Society in a new century of its life.

The foundation of the Society came at a time of intellectual ferment in Scotland, when Edinburgh could with justice claim a place of high distinction as a centre of learning and science. The men of the Enlightenment left for their successors a rich legacy of achievement in every field of learning and scientific inquiry. Of the fruits of the Enlightenment in Scotland not the least has been this Society.

There are however few institutions of lasting worth or influence whose structure has not been forged in the fires of dispute or controversy, and to these the Royal Society of Edinburgh was no exception, as the initial chapter of the record discloses. It was from a series of disputes, often conducted with some acrimony, that finally, by agreement between the Faculty of Advocates, the then Philosophical Society and the University of Edinburgh —whose Principal, the distinguished historian Dr William Robertson took a leading part in the eventually successful debates and discussions—the Royal Charter of 1783 was sought and granted 'for the advancement of learning and useful knowledge'.

And this history demonstrates how in the two centuries which have now passed since that Charter was granted the Society has fulfilled and is fulfilling these initial and fundamental purposes, even though not always with an equal degree of success, but never losing sight of those twin objectives. While the title of the Society is that of the 'Royal Society of Edinburgh', it is not to be thought that either in its origins or in its subsequent development and history the Society has in any sense been parochial, either in outlook or in recruitment to its Fellowship. As the authors recall, 'in the early years of the Society's existence many Fellows came from Glasgow, St Andrews, Aberdeen and elsewhere and happily, two hundred years later, the number is still widely distributed. The City of Edinburgh and its University not unnaturally have played the main role in the Society's history, but other cities and especially Glasgow have played their part.'

It must however always be kept in mind that the aim and purpose of the Society's founders and of those who have since guided and directed its affairs, was to provide a forum of discussion as well as a channel of communication—in no sense, as the authors state, 'a Society to be regarded merely as an association of select and exclusive experts and academics'. Indeed, such could not have been within the contemplation of the Society's founders in light of the diverse character of the associations and institutions which came together to form and to launch this great enterprise in the intellectual life of Scotland with its intended and actual impact on so many aspects of the world of practical affairs. The doors of the Society were therefore open and have remained open to 'all classes of men of research and intelligence' and the 'co-operation of men of all ranks, and of the most varied occupations and acquirements, was the very corner-stone of these institutions' (The Royal Societies of London and of Edinburgh) in the words of Principal Forbes in addressing the Society in 1862. The regard with which the Society had come to be held by that time in the wider world of affairs can be inferred from the comment of one of the greatest Scots lawyers of the nineteenth century and one of the most eminent Scotsmen of his day, who was also for many years Chancellor of Edinburgh University, Lord President Inglis —'the appointment of Presidency of the Royal Society of Edinburgh is one of the greatest honours that can be bestowed on any Scotsman in Scotland'.

It cannot be assumed that a Society with so long a history has escaped periods of lessened influence or impact, nor that all aspects of its purposes and activities will at all times be equally well served and promoted, and this Society has had its share of such variations, as the record demonstrates, not least in the field of letters; but the channels of communication and discussion have been kept open, and it may be will flow more amply in the years to come as the increase in emphasis on symposia of debate has added what may, and it is hoped will, be a valuable and natural development in the Society's services to learning.

The Society now faces the prospects and problems of a new century: our predecessors in 1883 may well have looked ahead with some confidence that the new century would record a further widening of the frontiers of knowledge, of a rich harvest of resulting benefit to mankind and a world in which the spread both of knowledge and understanding of the forces of nature would lead to greater security, material prosperity and moral growth. The actual record has fallen far short of what was for so many an expectation rather than a hope, an expectation which was in effect an article of faith. To scan the horizon in 1983 is to find it obscured by clouds of doubt and of uncertainty; for many observers it would seem this advance of the frontiers of science has not been marked by advances in human capacity to adjust to the powers revealed either in conduct or in ethics. That political and economic balance between East and West, which to the minds of the majority was a permanent element of life in the sunset of the nineteenth century, no longer seems to possess that assurance of permanence in the same degree today and even less for the decades to come.

At the same time, and as an almost inevitable consequence of the wider exploration and exploitation of the natural world and the universe itself, has followed a 'fragmentation' of skills and disciplines.

For the polymath or even for the educated Scotsman of scholarly tastes or inquiring mind of the era of Walter Scott, it was not too difficult to embrace within his ken the recognised fields of science, of philosophy and of letters: today the fields are of such extent that even the basic vocabulary of particular regions of knowledge and inquiry is a foreign tongue to those unable or unequipped to acquire it. Thus a paradox of life today and for the future; the greater expansion of the field of knowledge, the greater and more rapid the means of human communications, the less easily appear surmountable the barriers to understanding and to critical and informed discussion.

And yet civil society, and indeed the survival of civilised communities, depends in large measure upon the capacity of all its parts to achieve and share a common vocabulary of expression, and a common acceptance of certain assumptions as to the aims of that society and a measure of understanding as to the means and vehicles by which those aims can be achieved. The ever increasing pace of scientific exploration of the whole domain of the natural world, the constant extension of its frontiers, the urge of man 'to follow knowledge . . . beyond the utmost bound of human thought' compel, with much greater urgency than in that year when the Charter of this Society was granted, the fullest exchange and discussion of the fruits of that exploration.

The Royal Society of Edinburgh has throughout its history endeavoured, and with some measure of success to serve this need and it continues so to do. In collecting and preserving a library of scientific distinction and national importance it has served Scotland and the world of learning well, and by the incorporation of much of that library in Scotland's own National Library (itself a gift from the Faculty of Advocates, one of the founding agents of the Royal Society of Edinburgh) the Society has made further and vital contribution to that community of letters and learning which is of the cement of all civil society. Today, as the final chapters of this volume disclose, the Society, its vigour unabated, forges new links with the daily life of Scottish industry and of agencies of government and administration as well as continuing to provide a focus for debate and discussion in those disciplines which lie at the foundation of civilised life.

In discharging the task of recording this milestone in its history, and in calling to mind the illustrious work of its Fellows and their achievements, the authors in their labour of love, as it has been for them, and in particular Professor Campbell without whose careful and prolonged research this history could not have been prepared, have added yet another to the many services which over the years they have given so devotedly to the Society, its interests and its prosperity.

November 1982   JOHN CAMERON

Contents

List of Illustrations

LIST OF ILLUSTRATIONS

Authors' Preface

More than a hundred years ago Sir Robert Christison wrote (*Proceedings*, 1868, **6**, 393): 'The History of our Society has not yet been written. But it is a duty owing to our predecessors who earned for it a great reputation that some time soon a history should be written.' That history has not yet been written and it must be made clear that the present text does not fill the gap and makes no claim to be a complete annalistic account of the Society during its two hundred years' existence. It is rather a conspectus of some of the main events in the Society's history and of the exertions of those Fellows who devoted and still devote time and energy to promote the welfare of the Society. Necessarily the survey touches upon only a few of the multitudinous aspects, incidents and personalities of the Society, but it is hoped none the less that it provides a selective though not distorted presentation of the achievements of the Royal Society of Edinburgh and of that camaraderie and corporate spirit which have characterised the Fellowship from the beginning.

Emphasis has been laid on the Society not so much as an institution but as a gathering of men and women, many of whom have contributed to its activities and all of whom have been interested in scholarship and research. The authors will have achieved their purpose if these notes in the words of Professor David Hume (*Transactions*, 1785–89, **2**, 63) 'afford the means of rescuing from oblivion those of our members who, by their personal eminence and services, have merited the gratitude and remembrance of their country'.

Most of the book thus deals with the Society's past and its personalities, but the authors thought it desirable to include a chapter devoted to the present and the future. Chapter 7 it is hoped conveys something of the changes in the Society and its

House which will have considerable impact on the Society's future activities.

Readers are asked to note that all bibliographic references to the Society's principal publications (*Transactions* and *Proceedings*) are abbreviated throughout to *Trans.* and *Proc.* When a reference is made to a name currently on the Society's Roll the date of election is indicated. Where references are to former Fellows of the Society the years of birth and death are given.

The authors are deeply appreciative of the invaluable assistance so kindly given by Mr James Miller, Chairman, James Miller and Partners Ltd, Edinburgh, whereby financial support was secured towards the cost of printing this volume. A list of the contributing organisations will be found on pp. 185–86.

We are most grateful for permission to reproduce the following illustrations:

Sir David Brewster, University of St Andrews; James Clerk Maxwell with his mother, Cavendish Laboratory, Cambridge; James Hutton, Lord Bruntisfield; Lord Kelvin, Glasgow Museums and Art Galleries; Old College Library and William Robertson, University of Edinburgh.

It is quite impossible to thank all who have helped the authors in one way or another, but we would be ungrateful if we did not express our gratitude to Lord Cameron for writing a thoughtful Foreword and to Professor Emeritus Frank Bell, Professor W. W. Fletcher, Dr A. E. Ritchie and Dr W. P. Doyle for reading the whole manuscript and making valuable suggestions. Others who have given expert advice include Professors W. Cochran, I. N. Sneddon, G. Y. Craig, Dr C. D. Waterston and Mr D. M. Henderson. Finally, we have been greatly helped at all stages by Mr W. H. Rutherford and the Society's staff and by Mrs Marjory Campbell in the preparation of the indexes.

CHAPTER I

Origin, Aims and Development

Institutions comparable to the Royal Societies of London and Edinburgh can be traced back to the Italian Academies of the sixteenth and seventeenth centuries. At a time when the great masters such as Galileo, Copernicus, Tycho Brahe, Kepler and Leonardo da Vinci were laying the foundations of science as we know it today it is not surprising that not only literature and the fine arts but also the spirit of experiment and enquiry should give an impetus to the inauguration of learned societies. A lecture entitled 'The Royal Society of Edinburgh' given by Professor I. N. Sneddon (F.R.S.E., 1958) in Rome to the Accademia Nazionale dei Lincei, founded in 1603, serves to remind us that Italy was the home of the early learned societies in Europe. Another example is the Accademia Sectorum Naturae of Naples, founded in 1560. A century later, in 1660, the Royal Society of London was founded, emerging from the Society for the Cultivation of Natural and Experimental Science (1645). It was inevitable that the then comparatively recent invention of printing should result in the publication of journals for the wide dissemination of new discoveries and developments and on 1 March 1665 the Royal Society of London published *Philosophical Transactions*, the beginning of an unbroken series of publications, some of signal importance, which continue to the present day.

More than a century elapsed before the Royal Society of Edinburgh was founded in 1783, shortly before the Royal Irish Academy and the Académie des Sciences, Paris. It is of interest to note that the Académie des Sciences is a national institution with the salaries of the members paid by the State. In contrast the sister Societies on this side of the Channel are completely free from State influence although they have been and are generously helped by Government grants and other forms of support.

Principal Forbes of St Andrews University stated in an address that 'the germ of our Society is to be found in the Rankenian Club formed in 1716 for literary social meetings' (*Proc.*, 1862–63, 5, 7). It certainly provided a clear indication that there was a place in the Capital for a club whose members sought both the pursuit of knowledge and congenial fellowship. The Club met in Ranken's Inn, Edinburgh, and lasted for sixty years before its demise in 1774. It did not publish a journal, but it contained in its membership men such as Colin Maclaurin and Sir John Pringle, who later became President of the Royal Society of London.

More important than the Rankenian Club for the founding of the Royal Society of Edinburgh was the Society for the Improvement of Medical Knowledge instituted in 1731. Its Secretary was Dr Alexander Monro *primus*, first Professor of Anatomy in the University of Edinburgh and founder of the Edinburgh Medical School. The Society published five volumes of *Medical Essays and Observations*, which must have been of considerable importance since they were translated into several languages and may well have laid the foundations of the University's fame as a medical school. The *Essays* found favour with many distinguished scientists including Albrecht von Haller, the most influential physiologist of his time. In 1737 Colin Maclaurin proposed that literature and philosophy be included and the conjoint Society became the *Edinburgh Society for improving Arts and Sciences and particularly Natural Knowledge*[1] or, more shortly, *the Philosophical Society of Edinburgh*. Progress was hampered by the death of Maclaurin and the 1745 Rebellion, but in 1752 the Secretaries— David Hume and Alexander Monro *secundus*—were instructed to arrange papers for publication. As a result *Essays and Observations, Physical and Literary* appeared in 1754, to be followed by a second (1756) and a third volume (1771). Probably the best known contribution to the *Essays* is a chemical paper of fundamental importance by Joseph Black—his 'Experiments on Magnesia Alba' (p. 150).

The Philosophical Society, the immediate precursor of the Royal Society of Edinburgh, was a voluntary body 'liable to interruption and indeed dissolution' and towards the end of its existence it became lifeless and uncertain. The formation of a more permanent and comprehensive society, based 'upon a still more respectable footing and extensive scale, and comprehending not only medical and physical science, but every species of literary and philological discussion' was therefore sought and led to the formation of the Royal Society of Edinburgh.[2] The event was briefly described in *Transactions* (1788, **1**, 1): 'About the end of the year 1782 in a meeting of the Professors of the University of Edinburgh, many of whom were likewise members of the Philosophical Society and warmly attached to its interests, a scheme was proposed by the Rev. Dr Robertson, Principal of the University, for the establishment of a Society on a more extended plan, and after the model of some of the foreign academies, which have for their object the cultivation of every branch of science, erudition, and taste'. The plan was approved and adopted and a Royal Charter was sought.

This attractive picture of the establishment of the Royal Society of Edinburgh simply as the outcome of a civilised, sedate meeting of the Senatus of Edinburgh University, concerned only with the promotion of scholarship and research, gives no hint of the complex and sometimes far from edifying events, which preceded the Senatus meeting. As Steven Shapin brings out clearly in his informative and interesting *Thesis* (University of Pennsylvania, 1971: see also, *Brit. J. Hist. Sci.*, 1974, **7**, 1) the institution of the Society was preceded by a chain of events which arose from the decision in 1782 of the then recently formed Society of Antiquaries of Scotland to seek a Royal Charter. That Society, led by the eccentric and petulant Earl of Buchan,[3] had as its aim 'the cultivation of both antiquities and many aspects of general knowledge'. Among its proposed activities were lectures in natural history and the establishment of a natural history museum. Two bodies viewed these activities with suspicion and apprehension. The University was fearful that the mooted lectures on natural history given under the *aegis* of the proposed Society might rival those given in the University, and both the University and the Faculty of Advocates were uneasy at the prospect of the Society's museum functioning in competition with the University's museum and the Library of the Faculty of Advocates, which housed not only books and manuscripts, but also antiquarian objects. Chief among those particularly concerned at what was regarded as an encroachment of the Society of Antiquaries was John Walker (1751–1803), Professor of Natural

History in the University, and in 1782 he drew up a document entitled: 'Proposal for establishing at Edinburgh, a Society for the Advancement of Learning and Usefull Knowledge' (see John Walker papers in the Library of Edinburgh University). To achieve this Walker proposed that the University, the Faculty of Advocates, the Philosophical and Antiquarian Societies should unite to form the Royal Society of Edinburgh under a Charter from the Crown. Walker hoped in this way to denigrate the Society of Antiquaries with its rival museum and lectureship in natural history and as Shapin stresses there can be little doubt that 'the Royal Society of Edinburgh was Walker's invention devised to protect his professional and propriety interests'. Such a proposal was anathema to the Earl of Buchan and there were heated exchanges between the Society of Antiquaries on the one hand and the University and the Advocates on the other. October 1782 ushered in three months of great activity in which Henry Dundas, the Lord Advocate and Dean of the Faculty of Advocates, the Earl of Buchan, Principal Robertson, and Professors William Cullen, John Robison and John Walker participated, which ended with Dundas suggesting that a meeting between Buchan and Robertson might effect a reconciliation between the two parties. The meeting took place, but was a complete disaster.

The two bodies then went their separate ways and a request from William Cullen (1710–90), Professor of Medicine at Glasgow University and later of Chemistry and Physic at Edinburgh, and Vice-President of the Philosophical Society, that his Society join with the University of Edinburgh in forming a Royal Society took negotiations a step further. The Faculty of Advocates also favoured such a Society and the stage was set for the final act. Dundas and Sir James Hunter-Blair, City Member of Parliament, after consultations in London advised the Principal and Professors of the University to present a formal petition to the King: a petition for a 'Royal Society of Edinburgh for the Advancement of learning and useful knowledge'. The Senatus met on 30 November 1782, a petition was submitted to the King, and on 29 March 1783 the King's signature was obtained. On 6 May 1783, the Royal Charter and that of the Society of Antiquaries were extended under the Great Seal in Edinburgh.

The Royal Society of Edinburgh was thus founded as the outcome of great activity catalysed by intense controversy behind the scenes rather than by the impetus of cultural requirement. It was to be a Society with a liberal but ill-defined aim. The Society rapidly took shape and Robertson convened a meeting of petitioners on Monday, 23 June 1783,[4] in the College (University) Library. The assembly in terms of the Charter constituted itself as a meeting of the Royal Society of Edinburgh and elected the Hon. Thomas Miller of Barskimming, the Lord Justice Clerk, later Lord Glenlee (1717–89) to the Chair. The list of those present shows how representative was the gathering.

Thomas Miller	Lord Justice-Clerk
John Grieve	Lord Provost of Edinburgh
William Robertson	Principal, Edinburgh University
William Cullen	Professor, Edinburgh University
Alexander Monro *secundus*	Professor, Edinburgh University
John Walker	Professor, Edinburgh University
John Robison	Professor, Edinburgh University
Hugh Blair	Professor, Edinburgh University
Adam Ferguson	Professor, Edinburgh University
James Hunter-Blair	City Member of Parliament
Ilay Campbell	Solicitor General
Robert Cullen	Advocate
John Maclaurin	Advocate
William Nairne	Advocate
Adam Smith	Commissioner of Customs

The meeting 'resolved to constitute the assembly as a meeting of the Royal Society of Edinburgh' and proceeded to make the decisions necessary for running the Society. The Duke of Buccleuch was elected President and John Robison General Secretary and it was decided that all members of the Philosophical Society should be subsumed into Fellowship. Of the 60 members of the Philosophical Society in 1782, 58 became Fellows of the R.S.E., the Earl of Buchan, not surprisingly declining to join what he called an Omnium-Gatherum, while Lord Kames was removed by death in 1782. In addition invitations to join the Society were sent to 'a select number of other gentlemen' including the Lords of Council and Session, the Barons of the Exchequer and the Members (Professors) of each of the Universities of Scotland. Clearly the intention was to avoid the formation of a purely local Society and indeed the Royal Charter stipulated that '. . . a Literary Society be founded in Edinburgh suited to the state of that part of our realm which is called Scotland'. In the early years of the Society's existence many Fellows came from Glasgow, St Andrews, Aberdeen and elsewhere and happily two hundred years later the Membership is still widely distributed. The City of Edinburgh and its University not unnaturally have played the main role in the Society's history, but other cities and especially Glasgow have played their part.[5] Of the original Fellows Cullen, Black, Adam Smith and Hope all bore the Glasgow stamp, while Kelvin presided for many years when the Society's fortunes were at their peak. At the time of writing, the General Secretary and Treasurer are Glaswegians serving under an Aberdonian President.

On the understanding that it would be accommodated in University premises, the Society paid Edinburgh University £500. Space was allocated on the north side of the building, but the project came to nothing and some fifty years later Council was still seeking an explanation for the apparent breach of contract. Meantime, until 1807, the Society met in the University Library and later occasionally in the Physicians' Hall, George Street. In 1810 the Society purchased a house, 42 George Street, which it used until 1826, when under lease from the Trustees of the Board of Manufactures and Fisheries it was given the use of rooms in the Royal Institution in Princes Street (p. 18). The Society, it may be mentioned, was one of the bodies which proposed the erection of the Institution.[6] Walter Scott, at that period President of the Society, conceived: 'the new building to be a spur to the men of genius, knowledge and talents by whom he found himself surrounded so as to exert themselves on behalf of the Institution that it might not be said to have decreased in its literary and scientific fame while external circumstances attending its meetings were so much improved in elegance and convenience.' One is reminded of Crum Brown some hundred years later opening a new university chemistry department by remarking to his audience: 'A golden cage, but will the birds sing'! Be that as it may, the Society remained in the Royal Institution for more than 80 years until 1908 before moving, in 1909, into the present premises at 22, 24 George Street.[7] The move was effected by a Bill, 21 December 1906, in which the Government made funds available for the George Street house to be used rent free and to provide a grant of £600 per annum (p. 48).

6

With the foundation of the Society Edinburgh became the only city in Britain which possessed both an active scientific society and a university. This added to Edinburgh's unique cultural reputation as testified by many observers, two of whom may be cited. Benjamin Franklin (p. 17) asserted that the University of Edinburgh possessed a 'set of truly great men, Professors of Several Branches of Knowledge, as have ever appeared in any age or country',[8] while in 1789 Thomas Jefferson wrote that so far as science was concerned: 'no place in the world can pretend to competition with Edinburgh'. It is little wonder that the Society from the start flourished under such favourable conditions especially when the academics were strengthened by the legal and medical professions.

The Society of Antiquaries of Scotland on the other hand was soon in difficulties of one kind or another, but after many years 'in the wilderness' was revived largely by the efforts of Fellows of the Royal Society of Edinburgh. James Skene of Rubislaw, for example, acted as Curator of the two societies' museums, while Thomas Allan acted as Treasurer of both institutions. 'Battles of long ago' were finally forgotten when the two societies moved into the same building, first 42 George Street and then the Royal Institution (p. 48).[9]

The Society was originally divided into the Literary Class (93 members) and the Physical Class (72 members), the total number of founding members thus being 165. The Literary Class included in its ranks Adam Smith, Henry Mackenzie (1745–1831) ('The Man of Feeling', named after the title of one of his novels), and Mr (later Sir) Robert Liston, while the Physical Class included Joseph Black, James Hutton, James Watt, Clerk of Eldin, James Gregory, Dugald Stewart (1753–1828) and Sir James Hall. The number of Fellows varied as shown in the table:

1786	165
1790	223
1800	236
1810	198

For the first ten years both sections of the Society were active, and met separately on different days, each with a President and Secretary. Finally in 1828 the Society discontinued the practice of appointing a President and Secretary to each class and in 1832 separation of the Fellowship into the two classes also ceased. Sadly by this time the vigour of the Physical Class was not matched by that of the Literary Class and various reasons have been advanced for the different fortunes of the two Classes. The demise of the Literary Class was due, according to Principal Forbes, 'not from any disinclination of the Society to afford honourable room, but simply to a cessation of communications'. 'Perished of inanimation' was the pithy phrase used by Lord Moncreiff (*Proc.*, 1882–84, **12**, 451). Forbes amplified his statement by emphasising that: '. . . at no period could the literary papers bear comparison in point of merit, as a whole, with those of science. The great men of letters who lent the weight of their names to the institution, hardly maintained its reputation by their pens.' Even more forthright was Lord Moncreiff who stated that: '. . . The papers dwindled to somewhat pedantic dissertations on grammar, on modes of verbs, on pronouns, on the Greek letter signs, and were not animated in themselves nor likely to excite enthusiasm on a general audience.' It is both pleasant and significant to note that Forbes donned the mantle of prophet when he made the pronouncement: 'It is perfectly understood that a renewal of these classes (Literary Classes) would be considered to the Society.' These sentiments and hopes were later echoed by other Officers including David Milne Home, Douglas Maclagan (1812–1900) and Bishop Terrot (1790–1872). The last named was quite unequivocal in stating his belief that there was 'A general wish for some infusion of literature into our Proceedings' (*Proc.*, 1856, **3**, 398). Council was also concerned and expressed the view that there was 'a strong feeling among the Fellows that the next President should be a man of letters'. As a result the Lord Justice General, John Inglis (1810–91), was approached, but declined owing to pressure of other commitments (*Proc.*, 1891–92, **19**, xxi). In the event it was not until 1973 that the scientific chain was broken when the Society elected Lord Cameron to the Presidency. In the midst of these animadversions it is necessary to state that not all the scientific lectures and communications were interesting or meritorious. Robert Christison, for example, had some scathing things to say about the early medical papers read to the Society (p. 94) and some of the scientific papers border on the trivial. It is, however, significant that the *Edinburgh Review* (1802–03, **1**, 495–510) in discussing volume 5 of the *Transactions* commented unfavourably on the non-scientific articles therein (see also p. 24). It may here be interpolated that after nearly two centuries of 'inanimation' the Literary Class has been revived and once again is an integral part of the Society (p. 138).

From the beginning the Literary Class lacked any great on-going theme or themes. This was in sharp contrast to the Physical Class which in its important geological discussion and debate flourished and developed to make Edinburgh at that time a world centre of geological research with outstanding men such as James Hutton, Sir James Hall, John Playfair and Robert Jameson participating. In 1785 two meetings were devoted to a paper by Hutton, the first part being read by Black on account of Hutton's indisposition and the second by Hutton himself. The lengthy paper was entitled 'The Theory of the Earth' and on it modern geology is founded. It was first published in *Transactions*, 1788, **1**, 209, and later appeared in book form.[10] It is a matter of conjecture whether or not Hutton's 'Theory of the Earth' would have seen the light of day had the Society not come into being and Playfair's comments are perhaps pertinent: 'It might have been a long time before Hutton had given anything on this subject ('The Theory of the Earth') to the public, had not his zeal for supporting a recent institution which he thought of importance to the progress of science in his own country induced him to come forward, and to communicate to the Royal Society of Edinburgh a concise account of his theory of the earth.' (*Trans.*, 1805, **5**, 51.) The Society has reason to be proud of the fact that it provided the forum on which the 'Theory' was delivered and the *Transactions* by which it was communicated to the world.

Other early papers of fundamental importance in *Transactions* are two by Thomas C. Hope (p. 78) and one by Thomas Graham (p. 79).

Factors additional to inanimation (to use Lord Moncreiff's word) of the Literary Class caused the Society to develop largely into a scientific body (p. 8). Lord M'Laren[11] (1831–1910) (*Proc.*, 1889–90, **17**, 406) thought that science has an irresistible appeal and gave his opinion in the following words: 'A more true explanation of the comparative decline of pure scholarship and the preference of the more recondite and perhaps more laborious researches which are necessary for the development of scientific truth, may be found in this observation of E. Renan:—"The intense satisfaction attending scientific work arises from an assurance that the scientist feels that he labours at work which reposes on the eternal basis of fact, and of which the object at least is eternal,—a work that all civilised nations feel bound to pursue".'[12] To what degree the views of M'Laren and Renan are generally acceptable is perhaps open to discussion, but there can be no doubt that the Society's predilection to science was almost inevitable when it is remembered that the body mainly responsible for its formation namely, the Senatus of Edinburgh University, contained in its membership Dugald Stewart (1753–1828) (Moral Philosophy), John Robison (Natural Philosophy), John Playfair (Mathematics), John Walker (Natural History), Daniel Rutherford (Botany), James Gregory (Theory of Medicine), William Cullen (Practice of Medicine), Alexander Monro *secundus*, (Anatomy), and Joseph Black (Chemistry and Medicine).

An incisive remark by Goethe (1794–1832) that 'the most beautiful discoveries are made, not so much by men, as by period' suggests another factor in the emphasis on Science by the Society. The Society was formed at the beginning of a long period dominated by an intense interest in energy in general and heat in particular when men of the calibre of Hutton, Hall, Playfair, Brewster, Edward and J. D. Forbes, Clerk Maxwell, Tait and Kelvin were Fellows. Their contributions to science are to be found in many important papers in *Transactions* and *Proceedings*, some of which are mentioned in the following pages. In this connection one is struck by the number of scientific discoveries made by Fellows who attended the Edinburgh Medical School, but abandoned medicine for investigation in various scientific fields (see, e.g. p. 113). This suggests that the fame of the Medical School by attracting brilliant young men to the University was indirectly responsible for some of the notable scientific advances in the last century.

Although initially its long-term aims and objectives were somewhat nebulous, the Society had little difficulty in developing an acceptable programme to promote and stimulate the advancement of knowledge and to formulate the rules by means of which such a programme could be sustained. The three main objectives were:

1. To provide facilities for intercourse, personal and informal, between Fellows (p. 117).
2. To provide for the publication of periodicals (p. 31).
3. To provide a library and reading accommodation (p. 46). To these should be added a fourth provision, namely, that of awards in recognition of intellectual achievement. This has been met thanks to the generosity of a number of Fellows by means of medals and prizes (see p. 151).

It is generally acknowledged that the most important function of the Society is to afford a unique opportunity in Scotland for scientists and scholars of all disciplines and persuasions to meet. It thus acts not only as a 'mutual stimulus of association and discussion' (to use Sir Cyril Hinshelwood's expression), but also as an integrative influence. Richard Semon in 1899 wrote that 'science threatened to produce an unlimited number of specialists, each of whom is blind to everything but the narrow sphere of his chosen department'.[13] It is one of the functions of the Society to act as a corrective. It also helps to foster friendships between Fellows with widely differing interests and commitments and to this extent functions as a club (see also p. 146). In the early days no Society was required for Black, Hutton, Adam Smith, Adam Ferguson (1723–1816), John Home (1722–1808), Clerk of Eldin, George Clerk or Roebuck to meet. Few days would pass without these friends strolling and discoursing in the Meadows or Bruntsfield Links, but meetings of the Society provided this coterie with the means of discussing topics, some of prime importance, with other savants and of publishing the results of their deliberations. A hundred years later the same happy situation obtained (p. 49) with meetings of the Society attended by Kelvin and Tait (physicists), Crum Brown (chemist), Fleeming Jenkin (engineer), Turner (anatomist), Wyville Thomson (biologist), Lister (surgeon) and many others.

Special occasions and events leading to intimate inter-disciplinary collaboration are notably exemplified by the *Challenger* Expedition Commission responsible for investigating the huge collection of specimens gathered during the voyage and for publication of the results. The distinguished team which produced the monumental series of volumes (p. 114) included biologists, geologists, physicists and chemists: Wyville Thomson, John

Murray, P. G. Tait, Crum Brown, George Chrystal, William Turner and Archibald Geikie to mention a few.

It has always been accepted that an essential task of the Society is to bring to the notice of a wide public the results of experiment and discussion not only by lectures but also by the printed word. This was especially important in the early days when communication as we know it today simply did not exist. At a time when travel from Edinburgh to London took two days with a night stop at York, lack of communication was a source of much complaint and dissatisfaction and we read, for example, in the *Philosophical Magazine* (1841): '. . . but little of what is done abroad, especially in Germany, seems to find its way into England or at least until later after the lapse of some years.' It is therefore not surprising that shortly after its inauguration the Society published its *Transactions* and until 1797 papers from the Physical Class were separated from those of the Literary Class.

The Society has always recognised its international obligations. The *Transactions* and *Proceedings A* and *B* are sent to all parts of the world and it exchanges publications with more than 600 learned societies and institutions. The symposia are frequently attended by *savants* from overseas and the Society from time to time entertains visiting foreign delegations. Finally it is the Society's privilege and honour to elect Honorary Fellows from abroad as described on another page (p. 17).

Council at intervals reviews the Society's programme and considers shortcomings in its facilities (see, e.g. Sir Alfred Ewing, *Proc.*, 1925, **46**, 1; J. N. Davidson, *ibid.*, 1967, **70B**, 1; A. E. Ritchie in a thoughtful lecture to the Society entitled 'The Royal Society of Edinburgh—is it really necessary?', read on 31 October 1977). In the seventies urgent problems presented themselves and after careful consideration and intensive planning the Society embarked on a series of changes including reconstruction and renovation of the Society's House in George Street, the reestablishment of the Literary Class, and the transference or sale of most of the Library. Other changes such as the reintroduction of symposia have been made and with the major alterations are outlined in chapter seven.

The affairs of the Society have from the beginning been guided by an elected Council (p. 52), the composition of which with minor adjustments still obtains. Until 1828 each Class had a

President and Secretary, but thereafter these offices were abolished although the Secretaries continue as Secretaries to the Ordinary Meetings.

Few will dispute Lord Justice General John Inglis' statement that 'the appointment of Presidency of the Royal Society of Edinburgh is one of the greatest honours that can be bestowed on any Scotsman in Scotland'. The Presidency, however, is not only an honour but a commitment demanding a great expenditure of time and energy and the Society has been fortunate in always having men of calibre to fill the post. Originally the Presidents were elected annually, but in effect for life, and the first four Presidents officiated for a total period of 77 years.

The Duke of Buccleuch	appointed 1783(–1812)
Sir James Hall	appointed 1812(–1820)
Sir Walter Scott	appointed 1820(–1832)
Sir Thomas Makdougall Brisbane	appointed 1832(–1860)

The choice of Henry Scott, 3rd Duke of Buccleuch (1746–1812), as the first President of the Society, probably rested on his political association with the Lord Advocate, Henry Dundas, who chose him to speak to the King about the Society's request for a Royal Charter. It may well be that Dundas nominated him for the Presidency. Be that as it may, a change was effected in 1860 when the Society resolved to continue holding annual Presidential elections with the proviso that Presidents hold office for a period normally not exceeding five years. This practice has been followed except for Lord Kelvin who held office on three occasions— 1873–78, 1886–90, and 1895–1907—a total of 21 years. One interruption was the result of Kelvin's Presidency of the Royal Society of London. At the present time the President's period of office is normally three years.

Patronage

In the New Charter (1811) His Majesty George III declared himself Founder and Patron of the Society, but without committing his successors in any way. The Society accordingly has to request patronage from each monarch on succession to the throne.

Membership—Fellowship

The founders of the Society are to be congratulated on two counts: the generous view they took of the aims and objectives of the Society and of its Fellowship.[14] The aims of the Society have already been outlined (p. 10) and demonstrate that Principal Robertson and his colleagues were concerned that the Society should develop along liberal lines untrammelled by restrictive rules and regulations. With the Literary Class including in its province literature, philosophy, history, antiquities, speculative philosophy or other useful knowledge, and the Physical Class specifying mathematics, physics, chemistry, medicine and natural history it is clear that the Society's cultural range was very wide indeed. It is also certain that the Founders had no intention of forming a society to be regarded merely as an association of select and exclusive experts and academics. Evidence for this is found in the list of founding members and the point was made over and over again by Presidents and Officers. Principal Forbes in an address to the Society in 1862 said that persons who have no pretensions to science, art or literature should be eligible for Fellowship. 'I say, let them come, and freely, and let us regard their adhesion to our ranks as a compliment on either side. . . . The cooperation of men of all ranks, and of the most varied occupations and acquirements, was the very corner-stone of these institutions [The Royal Societies of London and of Edinburgh].' Dean Ramsay conveyed the same message in different words: 'The Royal Society is intended to attract and interest all classes of men of research and intelligence' (*Proc.*, 1861, **4**, 468) and Bishop Terrot also supported this view (*ibid.*, 1850–51, **3**, 402).

Forbes also recognised the importance of the social side of the Society and stressed that the Society should 'promote a cordial feeling among those who profess an interest in the progress of literature and science, and whose presence may make a contribution to this end'. He drove home his point by requesting: '. . . the more numerous portion of our Association, if they are not disposed to contribute papers to our meetings, at least to make a contribution of *themselves*, their mite of influence towards our commonwealth of letters.' On another occasion Forbes made the same point in a short pithy statement: 'There is something magnetic in a concourse of intelligent persons'. Neither must it be forgotten that not the least part of the Society's meetings is the opportunity afforded (in the old days) after and more recently before meetings for sociable intercourse. These informal gatherings over a cup of tea have long been an integral and pleasant part of the Society's programme and serve to remind us that Fellowship means something more than merely writing F.R.S.E. after one's name.[15] What is more delightful, for example, than to read about Clerk Maxwell's father (1787–1856), whose 'acme of felicity was to attend a meeting of the Royal Society of Edinburgh' (J. J. Thomson), in some instances accompanied by his son. It may be added that in 1836 Council recommended that 'by an earlier conclusion of the Private Business some time should be left for personal intercourse' and some twenty years later the General Secretary's report insisted that 'sittings must not be prolonged so as to interfere with the wish, generally felt, for conventional intercourse after the close of the regular business'.

It is not surprising that the main contributions to the Society's meetings and publications have come from those Fellows who are professional scientists (cf. however, p. 57), nor is it strange that the administration of the Society's affairs should be in the same hands. One has only to think of John Robison, David Brewster, James D. Forbes, Peter G. Tait, A. Crum Brown, Cargill Knott and William Turner (1832–1916) to realise the truth of this statement. Amateurs can however play a key role as exemplified by Sir John Robison (General Secretary, 1828–39) of whom Forbes said: 'under the favouring circumstances of affluence and leisure he conducted the affairs of the Society with more watchful and anxious superintendence than is often found in such cases—the care and direction of our affairs might be said to be his chief business'. Mention may also be made of those members of the Faculty of Advocates who have played a leading role in directing the fortunes of the Society—Sir Walter Scott, Lord Moncreiff and Lord Cameron. In addition to their Presidential duties Moncreiff (1811–95) and Cameron delivered notable addresses to the Society. Scott read no paper, but in 1831 his friend Skene read to the Society an extract from a letter written by Scott, partly at sea and partly at Malta, in which he gives an account of the newly formed volcanic Graham's Isle in the Mediterranean.

Admission to the Fellowship is governed by rules to be found in the Laws of the Society and for many years Fellows were introduced into the Society by signing the Roll Book and then shaking hands with the President. A certificate to which was attached a wax seal was then presented to the new Fellow. In 1861 Council decided that the President should in shaking hands address the Candidate in these words: 'In the name and by the authority of the Royal Society of Edinburgh, I admit you a Fellow thereof' and this formula still obtains.

For about 160 years the Laws of the Society decreed that 'the number of Fellows shall be unlimited' and Fellows were elected at the first meeting of each month. At these meetings a small number of candidates, each recommended by four Fellows and scrutinised by Council, were submitted and balloted for. This system of election in fact constituted a limitation of the Fellowship since the number of names brought forward seldom exceeded three or four. It is clear, however, that the Society opposed the election of members on the basis of original work only (see, e.g. Douglas Maclagan, *Proc.*, 1888–89, **16**, 2). A notable change of policy was effected in 1943 when Council decided to limit the number of recommended candidates at each annual election to 25. This method of election still obtains although the exact number admitted annually has occasionally been changed. At the time of writing it again stands at 25.

Examination of the records shows that until 1820 there was only a small variation in the number of Fellows (see table). This

1790	220	1890	450
1800	240	1900	520
1810	200	1910	630
1820	240	1920	630
1830	290	1930	700
1840	290	1940	760
1850	280	1950	790
1860	260	1960	750
1870	300	1970	780
1880	350	1980	850

(Numbers are 'rounded off')

began to change dramatically in the period 1820–30, the years of Scott's presidency. The increase in numbers, however, was probably due less to Scott's presence than to the energy and enthusiasm of the young General Secretary, David Brewster.

The last hundred years have witnessed a constant increase in the Fellowship triggered off by a striking rise in numbers immediately following 1870. It is difficult to dissociate this increase from the presence on Council of such devotees as Kelvin, Tait, Crum Brown and Christison. The most recent increase in the Fellowship is the direct result of the Society's renewed emphasis on 'arts and letters' and technology.

Honorary Fellows

From its foundation the Society has elected to its Fellowship Honorary Fellows, men and women who have rendered distinguished service to science and literature. The number of such Fellows was originally limited to twenty-one, but this was later changed to a maximum of 56, of whom not more than 20 were British subjects and 36 subjects of foreign states. These numbers were increased recently to 75, 25 and 50 respectively. Honorary Fellowship can also be conferred on Personages of Royal Blood.

    1820   King Leopold of the Belgians
    1849   Prince Albert
    1920   H.R.H. The Prince of Wales, later King Edward VIII
    1951   H.R.H. The Duke of Edinburgh
    1976   H.R.H. The Prince of Wales

One of the first Honorary Fellows to be elected was Benjamin Franklin (1706–90) and his election (1783) was happily recalled on 16 January 1956, when in the Society's rooms, Mr Eldred D. Kuppinger, United States Consul-General in Edinburgh, presented to the Society a Franklin Commemorative Medal from the Congress of the United States. The Medal was accepted on behalf of the Society by the President, Professor James Ritchie.

The list of Honorary Fellows contains the names of many figures in science or literature over the past two hundred years and includes those of Arago (1786–1853), Faraday (1791–1867), Berzelius (1779–1848), Carlyle (1795–1881), Tennyson (1809–92), Herschel (1792–1871), T. H. Huxley (1825–95) and John Stuart Mill (1806–73). Such names have conferred lustre on the award and some recipients have expressed their gratitude by delivering lectures or contributing papers to the Society. One Honorary Fellowship, which gave particular pleasure, was that awarded to Richard Anschütz (1853–1937), a distinguished

German chemist, for researches in which he demonstrated that 'in the history of organic chemistry the sorely tried Archibald Scott Couper deserves a place beside his more fortunate fellow worker, Friedrich August Kekulé'. Anschütz described how with the help of Crum Brown he proved that Couper, a native of Kirkintilloch, in 1858, two months before Kekulé, had stated simply and clearly the theory on which modern organic chemistry rests (*Proc.*, 1909, **29**, 193). In Couper's own words:

[Carbon] combines with equal numbers of equivalents of hydrogen, chlorine, oxygen, sulphur, etc.

It enters into combination with itself. These two propositions in my opinion explain all that is characteristic of organic chemistry.

Couper worked with Würtz in Paris and submitted his paper to him for publication, but Würtz delayed presenting it to the French Academy with the result that it was read two months after the appearance of Kekulé's famous paper. Kekulé gained world-wide admiration and Couper remained unknown. When Kekulé later learned the true state of affairs he was not ungenerous to Couper, but insisted on his own priority. Couper retired a broken man to his native land and little was heard of him until some fifty years later justice was served by the publication of Anschütz's paper.

Two other Honorary Fellows may perhaps be mentioned: Goethe, who was elected during the period of Walter Scott's presidency, not for his literary but for his scientific ability, and Robert Wilhelm Bunsen (1811–99), one of the greatest chemists of the nineteenth century. Of the latter John Read, Professor of Chemistry at St Andrews University, used to delight in telling the following anecdote. Bunsen's lecture room in Heidelberg contained a large upright pillar. Now Bunsen had to sign attendance cards of those students who took his class and in his good natured way he usually endorsed the card: 'mit ausgeichnetem Fleiss' ('with great industry'). On one occasion, failing to recognise one applicant Bunsen exclaimed: 'Aber, Herr Dingskirch, ich habe Sie in der Vorlesung gar nicht gesehen' ('but I've never seen you at a lecture'). 'Ja, Herr Geheimrath' replied the student 'ich sitze immer hinter dem Pfeiler' ('Indeed, Herr Geheimrath, but you see I always sit behind the pillar'.). 'Ach' said Bunsen sadly 'da sitzen so viele' ('Ah, what a lot of you sit there'.). He reached for the certificate, signed it, and endorsed it 'mit ausgeichnetem Fleiss'.

It is to the credit of the Society that during the two World Wars it did not suffer from war fever and remove from the Roll those Foreign Honorary Fellows who belonged to enemy countries. The only action taken was at the end of the First World War to remove the names of those Foreign Honorary Fellows who had publicly renounced such honours from British learned societies.

Notes

1 In the Society's Library is a copy of an autograph letter presented to the Society by Karl Pearson (1857–1936; Hon. F.R.S.E., 1934) in which Colin Maclaurin on 7 June 1737, described the foundation of the Edinburgh Society for improving Arts and Sciences.

2 Cullen in a letter (14 December 1782) to Henry Dundas, then Lord Advocate, states: '. . . the Philosophical Society have many reasons for desiring to be formed into a body corporate . . . they are willing and desirous to be comprehended in an institution which, they think will be, of general utility and credit to the country'.

3 According to Lord Neaves, David Steuart Erskine, 11th Earl of Buchan 'with some peculiarities of character, was a man inspired by a sincere zeal for the advancement of literature and science'. This generous assessment was echoed by R. P. Gillies in his *Reminiscences of a Literary Veteran*, who admitted that the Earl 'wandered far from the paths of common sense', but 'was quite sincere in all his vagaries'. For a balanced assessment of the Earl's life and character see R. G. Cant in *The Scottish Antiquarian Tradition* (John Donald, Edinburgh, 1981).

4 The first meeting attended by those who had accepted Fellowship was held on 4 August 1783. Here the proposed Laws were enacted and arrangements made for the 1st meeting of the Physical Class on 4 November 1783 (p. 5).

5 'Inter-city rivalry or jealousy is as foreign to its [R.S.E.] history as are the forbidden topics of religion or politics' (*Glasgow Herald*, 8 December 1906).

6 In November 1821 on the proposal of Henry Mackenzie at a meeting of the Society a committee was appointed to communicate with the Board of Trustees of Manufactures and Fisheries, the Highland and Agricultural Society of Scotland, the Institution for the Encouragement of the Fine Arts and the Society of Antiquaries of Scotland to stress that the erection of a Common Building at the Mound would be advantageous to the Society and the City. In the event the Board of Trustees, a quango, in receipt of an annual national subvention, commissioned William Playfair (1789–1857) to design a suitable building. This was erected in due course and housed, as tenants of the Board, the Society, the Society of Antiquaries, and the Royal Institution for the Encouragement of the Fine Arts. The abbreviated title of the last named body was

applied to the building itself which thus became known as the Royal Institution until 1911 when it was renamed the Royal Scottish Academy.

7 The last meeting of the Society in the Royal Institution was held on 26 October 1908 and the first in 22, 24 George Street on 1 March 1909. In the interim the Society met in University premises at High School Yards.

8 Edinburgh also figures in Benjamin Franklin's 'Autobiography' where he states that: 'Persons of good sense I have since observed, seldom fall into argument, except lawyers, university men, and men of all sorts that have been bred at Edinburgh'. [Scott in his Journal refers to 'The Edinburgh *pruritus disputandi*'.]

9 In 1851 the Antiquarian Society's collection of antiquities was transferred as a gift to the nation and is now housed in the National Museum of Antiquities in Queen Street, Edinburgh. See *The Scottish Antiquarian Tradition*, edited by A. S. Bell (John Donald, Edinburgh, 1981).

10 A facsimile of the *Theory of the Earth* was produced in 1970 by the Hafner Publishing Company with an introduction by V. A. Eyles.

11 Lord M'Laren presided 'at the meetings of the Society and Council on more occasions than had fallen to the lot of any other Fellow' (Council Minutes, 16 May 1910).

12 See also H. A. L. Fisher in his *A History of Europe*: 'Science is a growing thing, which gives it an interest and impetus which is irresistible.'

13 Sir Samuel Curran, however, has warned the Society 'not to criticise over-severely the specialists among us' (*Year Book*, 1962, p. 5).

14 For many years the terms 'Fellow' and 'Member' seem to have been used indiscriminately. The first volume of *Transactions*, for example, gives a list of Members and Fellows and the Laws enacted in 1811 state that 'The Royal Society of Edinburgh shall be composed of Ordinary and Honorary Members'. The decision to abandon the word 'Member' was taken about the middle of the last century.

15 Two side-notes on the use of 'F.R.S.E.'. According to a Council Minute (1 July 1935): 'F.R.S.E. should not be used in any way which might savour of advertisement.' In another Minute (19 June 1922) a disgruntled Fellow is taken to task for an article in *Nature* in which he stated that 'we may not feel very proud to add the letters F.R.S.E. after one's name'.

CHAPTER II

Meetings, Publications and Library

As related earlier the Society was founded with no precise formulation of its aims and objectives, but it seems to have been taken for granted that the Society was committed to organise lectures, arrange for the production and publication of learned journals, and maintain a library (p. 35). These commitments were implemented and their development is outlined in the following pages

Meetings

How many younger workers have caught their inspiration from contact with these older workers who have long been among us? How many have been drawn out and cheered on by associations in this room?

Kelland, *Proc.*, 1878–79, **10**, 34

Not the least important of the Society's activities are the Ordinary Meetings held in the Society's rooms, most of which have been and still are held on Mondays, and each year has seen a programme of lectures given once or twice a month. It was long recognised, however, that Fellows and their friends who do not live in Edinburgh might find meetings outside the city more acceptable and four such meetings were held:

Perth	26 February 1963
Kelso	1 April 1964
Inverness	4 June 1965
Stirling	5 October 1966

The meetings were only partially successful. In 1980 two Regional Meetings were held in Aberdeen and one in Glasgow when the President outlined future developments and the General Secretary gave a talk on the history of the Society. With these and a few other exceptions all the Society's meetings between 1909 and 1981 have been held in the George Street House.

In the early days of the Society the Physical and Literary Classes met on different days (p. 7), but the demarcation between the two was far from rigid. Andrew Duncan *senior*, Professor of the Theory of Medicine in Edinburgh University, for example, was a keen antiquarian and frequently chaired meetings of the Literary Class, while Lord Meadowbank (1748–1816), an advocate, sometimes chaired the Physical Class meetings. Lecturers also did not find themselves bound to one class and examples of cross-discipline were James Hall's paper on 'The Origins and Principles of Gothic Architecture', James Hutton's paper on 'Written Language', and Professor James Gregory's 'Thesis on the Moods of Verbs'. As already described (p. 7) the Literary Class dwindled away so that the Society became primarily a scientific body. Thereafter only occasional papers other than scientific are to be found in the Society's publications, notable among which are Henry Mackenzie's 'Account of the German Theatre' (p. 124), Stuart Blackie's 'Latest Phases of Literary Style in Greece', D'Arcy Thompson's 'Bird and Beast in Ancient Symbolism' and Melville Clark's 'Sir Walter Scott' (p. 124), a model lecture which, along with the ovation accorded to the lecturer, will long be remembered by those privileged to hear it.

The Society's records give disappointingly little information about the meetings and lectures in the early days, but suffice to show that the topics varied from the important to the trivial (p. 94). There are indications, however that speakers were carefully selected and we read, for instance, in the Council Minutes of 19 April 1824, that 'Mr Russell and Dr Hope reported that Mr Buchan of Hull's paper was not of sufficient importance to be read to the Society'. On the other hand some of the lectures were of outstanding interest and include those given by Sir James Hall on Lavoisier's theory of combustion (4 February, 3 March and 7 April 1788) followed by Hutton (5 and 12 May 1788; 7 March 1791). As Hall accepted Lavoisier's theory, while Hutton remained a phlogistonist, these lectures must have been attended by sharp if reasoned controversy. It is tantalising to know so little about these lectures given at a time of crucial change in chemical thought (p. 79) and Hall's lectures may well have been the first account in this country of Lavoisier's new theory of

chemistry. Failure to publish them is attributable to the partici-
pants for we read that Sir James Hall 'did not incline that his
paper or any abstract of it should be printed in this volume [of
Transactions]'. The Wernerian and Hutton geognosies likewise
gave rise to lively meetings (1807–09) with Jameson leading with
'great talent and energy' (Christison). Thomson is also reported
as taking a prominent part in 'these important and harmoniously
conducted discussions' (*Edin. New Phil. J.*, 1852–53, **54**, 86).
This perhaps does not quite accord with Sir James Hall's description of the discussions 'which *raged* within these halls' or with
Thomson's fiery temperament.

If in the early years many of the meetings were interesting and
stimulating there have been other periods when the Society, to
use Douglas Maclagan's words (*Proc.*, 1889–90, **17**, 4) 'like other
similar bodies has had its periods of scientific famine and mournful
inactivity'. This is confirmed by an earlier statement by Brewster
(*Proc.*, 1865, **5**, 322): 'The regular meetings of the Society had
frequently no other business than to read the minutes, elect
members, and receive donations and this was sometimes done in
the presence of only one Secretary and one or two members of
Council. In such circumstances the Secretary summoned the
meeting by a billet printed in red ink when a paper was to be read,
and one in black when he had nothing to communicate'. In 1797
and 1798 on several days scheduled for a meeting no meeting was
in fact held. There is little evidence as to the attendance at those
early meetings, but it is probable that twenty or so was the
average.

The reason for this unsatisfactory state of affairs is not hard to
seek. For many decades the Society's meetings programme comprised a Statutory Meeting on the last Monday of October when
the Council was elected and this was followed by a series of
Ordinary Meetings. The programme at each meeting followed a
general pattern: two or more communications from Fellows or
occasionally from *savants* from abroad or south of the Border and
frequently one or two Fellows were elected. With little knowledge of science many Fellows must have been profoundly bored
and discouraged from attendance. Walter Scott admitted attending
a meeting of the Society without understanding a word of the
lecture and many years later Bishop Terrot opined that: '. . . the
proceedings of our meetings possess little attraction for the

greater portion of our Fellows.' It was not always the subject matter which was to blame for we read in *Proceedings* (1875, **9**, 25) that: 'John Sinclair (1797–1875) was selected by the Council to endeavour to induce Archdeacon John Williams (1792–1858), Rector of the Edinburgh Academy, to shorten the length of a paper he was to read on Greek participles, a subject on which he had read several papers before, much to the *ennui* of the majority of members'.[1] It is a little ironic that such a task should be remitted to the son of Sir John Sinclair (p. 60), whom Scott regarded as a 'prince of Bores'.

In an effort to provide more interesting meetings Council eventually decided (21 December 1863) to invite Fellows to give outlines of the 'Business they Profess'. As a result lectures were given by Lyon Playfair (1818–98) on 'Coal Tar Colours', by Tait on 'The Conservation of Energy', and by Piazzi Smyth on 'Recent Measurements at the Great Pyramid and the Deductions flowing therefrom' (p. 70). A lecture by Lyon Playfair 'On the Diet of the Royal Engineers stationed at Chatham' made sufficient impact to be remembered years later in a song by Douglas Maclagan (p. 147). These lectures gave some 'body' to the proceedings which the shorter, more specialised papers did not. Nonetheless shorter communications continued to dominate the meetings until 1949 when, largely at Kendall's instigation (p. 50), it was decided to take smaller communications 'as read' and to make the main business the reading of a single address on a major topic of general interest, frequently by a guest speaker. This has proved to be acceptable and still obtains.

Until about 1890 obituary notices of deceased prominent Fellows were read at Ordinary Meetings and some of these are to be found in *Transactions* and *Proceedings*, particularly in the earlier volumes. There are, however, some notable omissions with no notices worthy of the name being printed for Scott, Kelvin or Brewster, and Brewster took some blame for lack of memoirs of Dugald Stewart, John Playfair, and James Hall (*Proc.*, 1864–65, **6**, 321). Some of the notices are lengthy and are of considerable historical value (p. 33). Later notices while often shorter contain much interesting information and one in particular calls for special attention. This is the bizarre *éloge* read to the Society on 3 December 1877, by Piazzi Smyth (1819–1900) to commemorate an Honorary Fellow and famous French astronomer,

Le Verrier (*Proc.*, 1877–78, **9**, 489). Le Verrier was a brilliant but temperamental scientist, an egotist who was paranoic if his observations and conclusions were doubted or criticised. There were consequently unhappy incidents in his career calling for discrete abbreviation or omission in any notice about him. It would have been well if Piazzi Smyth had obeyed the dictum of Robert Chambers (*The Book of Days*, 1861) that: 'Biography, combining instruction and amusement, not infrequently exhibits, in one and the same character, examples of excellence to be fearlessly followed and weaknesses to be sedulously shunned'. Such sedulous shunning was quite beyond Piazzi Smyth, who while eulogising Le Verrier in the earlier parts of the *eloge* later was disconcertingly expansive on two episodes. Le Verrier had crossed swords with a gifted mathematician, Delaunay, who gave the value of 8.85″ for the Solar parallax and proved Le Verrier's value of 8.95″ to be incorrect. Piazzi Smyth takes up the story: 'Their discussions, meeting after meeting of the Academy, attained a vigour and an intensity which drew half Paris to *assist* at these reunions: but chiefly to hear Le Verrier. He was indeed scientifically in the wrong: and had, long afterwards to modify his 8.95″ to something very close to Delaunay's number. But what did the crowd care for minute exactitudes. They went to see how a hero fights, how he gains his successes: and Le Verrier gave them plenty of that. . . . On such occasions Le Verrier seemed to float in positive pleasure throughout the combat, cutting down his enemies with ease on every side'. For a while Le Verrier flourished as Director of the Paris Observatory, but he ran into difficulties by not according to his able assistants recognition of their work and by claiming their results as his own. Yet as Piazzi Smyth points out: 'with every successive conquest, Le Verrier was making a wider and wider void for himself: until with one dazzling victory more,—there came the news that every one had left him, and the Director of the Observatory [Le Verrier] reigned alone over his telescopes. The Minister of the Interior then had to step in and give a disorganising Director his dismissal.' Piazzi Smyth's style is unmistakeable and it is little wonder that the *eloge* was recalled some thirty years later by Cargill Knott.

If the question were posed, what was the most memorable and liveliest meeting ever held in the Society's rooms the answer without doubt would be that held on 4 December 1837, when Mr John Stark, a printer and naturalist, read a paper entitled 'Notice on the Food of the Herring and Salmon'.[2] This subject seems in-occuous enough, but it had been rumoured that the lecture would 'contain an exposure of Dr Knox's plagiarism and reckless-ness of statement' in a lecture he had given earlier (*Trans.*, 1833–36, **12**, 462). Sir Thomas Makdougall Brisbane occupied the Chair and Stark duly delivered his address in which he was highly critical of Knox's earlier statements and disputed Knox's claims to precedence of discovery. If we are to believe the account of the meeting given in *Proceedings* (1837–38, **1**, 169) little worthy of special comment is necessary. Very different, however, is the story told by Henry Lonsdale, a pupil and colleague of Knox, in his book *Life and Writings of Robert Knox*. Knox apparently waited until Stark had finished, then rose and began his defence by saying: 'Is it necessary for me, Sir Thomas, the friend and com-panion of Baron Cuvier, to defend himself in the society of my compeers against the base and personal scurrilities of a mere dabbler in science?' He then proceeded with all the forensic wit and invective at his command to vent his wrath upon the hapless Mr Stark. His 'force of eloquence and pointed satire such as had never been heard within the walls of the Society were received throughout with roars of laughter and applause'. Others who ventured to argue with Knox were Professors Traill, Christison and Syme and they too were similarly mauled and vanquished. The meeting finished with 'The Anatomist, armed with all his weapons—a polished satire more keen and incisive than any Damascus blade in Saracen's hands—cutting right and left, smiting his enemies hip and thigh'.[3] Stark must have regretted his entry into the polemical field.

Fortunately for the reputation of the Society there has been no repetition of anything resembling the exciting but unedifying Stark—Knox meeting and the Ordinary Meetings are conducted with decorum though with the minimum of pomp and ceremony. The lectures delivered at these meetings, as pointed out by Dr A. E. Ritchie in his conspectus of the Society's activities (p. 12), are characterised by *quality* and are given by men or women who are masters of their subject. It would be idle to pretend that all have *appeal*, i.e. that all are both informative and interesting, but it must be recognised that the Society's lecturers are faced with the daunting problem of having to address an audience many of whom are quite ignorant of the subject and its terminology. It may be remarked that Hutton in his two great lectures to the Society (p. 9) overcame this difficulty by completely avoiding jargon, i.e. the employment of technical words not commonly intelligible. Be that as it may, present-day Fellows can look back on many lectures of absorbing interest, some of which are mentioned elsewhere in the text (e.g. pp. 22, 126 and 128).

Occasionally the Society holds meetings to celebrate particular events and honour distinguished Fellows and Scholars, and on 7 May 1934 celebrated its 150th anniversary with an address by D'Arcy Thompson entitled 'Fifty Years Ago', which drew a large audience and 'taxed to the utmost the accommodation at 22 George Street'. Fittingly this was followed by a Civic Reception in the Royal Scottish Academy, the building which had housed the Society for more than 80 years (p. 6). The history of the Society had previously been the subject of addresses by Principal Forbes on 1 December 1862 (*Trans.*, General Index, 1783–1888, p. 15) and by Sir William Turner on 8 November 1909 at the opening of the Society's 'new home' in George Street (*ibid.*, 1889–1908, p. 1).

Other notable events include:

> 24 July 1914. The International Congress to celebrate the tercentenary of John Napier's *Mirifici Logarithmorum Canonis Descriptio* (p. 34).
>
> 4 July 1938. The James Gregory Tercentenary celebrations, held at the invitation of the Society in 22 George Street (p. 34).
>
> 28 May 1943. The Quatercentenary Commemoration of the death of Nicolaus Copernicus when lectures were delivered by Professors E. T. Whittaker and W. M. H. Greaves in the presence of the President of the Republic of Poland, M. Władysław Racziewicz.
>
> 3 March 1947. On the anniversary of the birth of Edinburgh born Alexander Graham Bell a lecture was given by Professor G. W. O. Howe entitled 'Alexander Graham Bell and the invention of the Telephone'.
>
> 3 November 1947. The Society along with other Societies organised a series of lectures by Sir Edward Bailey, Dr Murray MacGregor (1884–1966), Dr V. A. Eyles (1895–1978), Dr G. W. Tyrrell (1883–1961), and Dr S. I. Tomkeieff (1892–1968) to commemorate 150 years since the death of James Hutton. A

memorial plaque was built into the wall of Greyfriars Church-yard at a ceremony headed by Lord Provost Falconer (*Proc.*, 1950, **63B**, 357).

3 December 1956. The Hugh Miller Centenary was marked by a lecture by Professor T. S. Westoll (F.R.S.E., 1943) entitled 'Hugh Miller and the Old red Sandstone'.

12 October 1976. The Universities of Edinburgh and Heriot-Watt combined with the Society to organise a lecture to mark the bicentenary of the publication of Adam Smith's *The Wealth of Nations*. The lecture was given in the George Square Theatre by Professor T. L. Johnston (*Yearbook*, 1977, p. 5).

12 November 1979. The Centenary of the death of Clerk Maxwell was to be marked by a lecture by Professor R. V. Jones, but delay on the railway journey from Aberdeen to Edinburgh prevented him delivering it (p. 109). At very short notice Professor W. Cochran stepped into the breach and gave a most interesting and informative lecture.

Thanks to the good offices of one of the Fellows, Mr Harry Hoggan (1905–82) of the British Broadcasting Corporation, a documentary programme of the Society's activities was shown on Thursday, 5 October 1967. The transmission in necessarily truncated form conveyed something of the scope and spirit of the Society's aims and functions.

During the last thirty years the Society's efforts to bring to the notice of Fellows the significance and application of recent discoveries and inventions are evidenced by the Society's lecture programmes, some pertinent examples of which are:

1 May 1944 'The Electron Microscope' by Professor G. D. Preston (1896–1972)

26 October 1959 'DNA (Deoxyribonucleic Acid)' by Dr F. H. C. Crick (Hon. F.R.S.E., 1966)

7 December 1964 'The Place of the Computer in the University' by Dr D. C. Gilles (F.R.S.E., 1964)

2 March 1970 'The Float Glass Process' by Sir Alastair Pilkington (p. 117).

23 October 1976 'Geothermal Energy' by Sir Kingsley Dunham (F.R.S.E., 1971) (Bruce-Preller Lecture).

5 February 1979 'Laser Light' by Professor R. A. Smith (1909–80) (*Yearbook*, 1979, 5).

To bring advances in recent research and scholarship to the notice of schoolboys and schoolgirls Council in 1980 decided to establish a series of Christmas Lectures to be delivered at different centres in Scotland (p. 141).

It appears that (pp. 111, 118) interest in current topics has not always prevailed within the Society's walls and one cannot fail to be struck by the incuriosity of the Fellowship to Fox Talbot's invention of the calotype photographic process in 1837, surely an event of great significance in science and civilisation. It appears that the subject was not discussed at any of the Society's meetings until 1852, which is all the more surprising since Fox Talbot was a Fellow and his friend, David Brewster, was a photography enthusiast.[4] Other years when events of the utmost importance in science passed unnoticed include 1858 when the Italian chemist Cannizzaro published his famous paper and opened up a new era of chemistry. It is only fair to state, however, that Alexander Graham Bell's invention of the telephone in 1876 was followed in a short time by a number of papers on the subject by Tait, George Forbes, Chrystal and the ingenious experiments and microphones by James Blyth, then mathematical master in George Watson's Boys' College. In another field the Duke of Argyll in his Presidential Address (*Proc.*, 1857–62, **4**, 350) showed his percipience in 1860 by stressing the importance of Darwin's *Origin of Species* which had been published the year before. Perhaps the best example of the Society's interest in current affairs is found in the Society's meetings in 1788 (p. 22) when chemistry was emerging as a science.

Conversaziones

Periodically the Society organises conversaziones where Fellows and their friends can meet socially and at the same time view exhibits and demonstrations on display. The records show that long intervals separated the early conversaziones or soirées but since the Second Great War eight have been held, all successful with attendances varying between 300 and 600. Opportunity for school boys and girls to view the exhibits has proved to be very rewarding.

22 May 1959	Adam House, University of Edinburgh
24 June 1960	Royal Botanic Garden, Edinburgh
8 June 1962	School of Agriculture, Edinburgh
7 July 1967	Appleton Tower, University of Edinburgh

30 May 1969	Mountbatten Building, Heriot-Watt University, Edinburgh
7 May 1971	Hunter Halls, University of Glasgow
4 April 1975	University of Dundee
30 May 1979	Riccarton Campus, Heriot-Watt University, Edinburgh

For more than 150 years the R.S.E. was a men's Society and although this was never explicitly admitted Council on one occasion ungallantly decided to exclude ladies from their conversazione. Fortunately, better counsels later prevailed and ladies for the last 100 years have graced the Society's meetings although it was not until 1949 that they were admitted to Fellowship (p. 50). The appointment in 1981 of Professor (Emeritus) Anna MacLeod (F.R.S.E., 1962) to Council marks a further break with tradition.

Symposia

In recent years considerable emphasis has been placed on the organisation of symposia and in the event these have proved to be very successful. Some idea of the range and variety of the topics presented may be gained from the following random list:

4 May 1959   Immunological Tolerance

15 May 1967   Biological Effects of Ionising Radiation. Organised by Professor Robert McWhirter (F.R.S.E., 1944). *Proceedings*, 1968, **70B**, 117–162.

12 May 1969   Anti-lymphocytic Antibody. Organised by Sir Michael Woodruff (F.R.S.E., 1958)

4 February 1972   Blood and Blood Products. Chairmen: J. Halliday Croom and Sir Maurice Yonge. *Proceedings*, 1972, **71B**, S1–S93

29 October 1972   The Forth-Tay Estuaries. An Environmental Assessment. Organised by Dr L. J. Hale. *Proceedings*, 1972, **71B**, 97–224

3–6 April 1973   Simple Nervous Systems. Held in Glasgow in co-operation with the Scottish Electro-physiological Society

11–13 June 1973   The Loch Leven Project. Held in the University of Stirling. *Proceedings*, 1972–74, **74B**

26–27 April 1976   Scottish Science Education. Held in the Lecture Theatre of the Royal Botanic Garden, Edinburgh

10 January 1977   Biodegradability

5 May 1977 Experimental Carcinogenesis. With the Royal College of Physicians, Edinburgh

13 May 1977 Inter-relations between Forestry and Agriculture in the Uplands of Scotland

11–12 October 1977 The Natural Environment of the Outer Hebrides. *Proceedings*, 1979, **77B**

17 March 1978 Scottish Mountain Weather. With the Royal Meteorological Society

24–26 September 1980 Energy in the 90s. With the Highlands and Islands Development Board.

In each symposium lectures are given on topics of particular interest or controversy and opportunity is afforded for discussion and debate.

Publications

Hence the importance of publication. It is at once the food of existing thought and the seed of future knowledge.

Professor Kelland. Opening Address to the Society, 6 December 1858.

Five years after the founding of the Society the first volume of *Transactions* appeared (1788), thus launching a journal which after a hesitant start has appeared at intervals ever since. Council, however, made it clear that it did not anticipate that all addresses to the Society would be published and amplified this by rather engagingly stating: 'It is not, however, to be understood that these papers which do not appear in *Transactions* of the Society are thought unfit for the public eye. Several papers have been communicated with the sole purpose of furnishing an occasional entertainment to the members, and this end being attained, have been withdrawn by the authors' (*Trans.*, 1788, **1**, 14). To our regret Hutton and Hall and others have sometimes so acted (p. 23) and occasionally feelings of delicacy or fear of giving offence have caused Fellows to delay publication of their investigations (p. 86).[5]

The publication of scientific papers was often subject to difficulties and delays and especially in the early days of the Society the publication of *Transactions* was far from smooth and regular. Brewster complained that in each of the years 1799, 1802, 1803, 1808 and 1809 only one of the papers read at the Society's meetings appeared in *Transactions* and in the years 1801 and 1806 not a single paper appeared. This unsatisfactory state of affairs was probably partly due to what Douglas Maclagan termed the 'very languid condition' of the Society at the beginning of the century (*Proc.*, 1888–89, **16,** 2) and partly to the lack of a permanent full-time official on the Staff, so that the editorial duties fell largely on the shoulders of the over-worked General Secretary (p. 54). Matters improved, but in the 1840s the appearance of successive volumes of *Transactions* could still be separated by four years. However J. D. Forbes, in his 7th Annual Report, stated that: '. . . no publishing scientific society either at home or abroad with the exception of the Royal Society of London issues its publications with the same punctionality as ours.' This rosy picture does not seem to have been sustained for long and in 1857 Christison was complaining that interest in the Society was lessened by 'tardiness of publication'. In spite of this it is undeniable that Kelvin, Forbes, Brewster and many others published some of their important papers in *Transactions* and *Proceedings*, journals which formed the favourite publication media for Tait and Crum Brown. There was thus considerable justification for Kelland's considered opinion that: 'Our *Transactions* of the present period contain papers not a few of which are destined to take their place in the permanent repertoires of science' (*Proc.*, 1878–79, **10,** 34).

The selection of papers for publication has always been an important responsibility of Council (*Trans.*, 1788, **1,** 14), who have for many decades appointed 'members conversant with the subject' to act as referees and there are many indications that referees have been most conscientious, helpful and when necessary critical. Clerk Maxwell, for example, took his refereeing duties very seriously and in lengthy reports generously indicated how weak points in a paper could be amended. Other referees frequently were more terse, one, finding that 'the language is often inaccurate and not infrequently very obscure' and recommending that the paper be rewritten. There were, of course, the inevitable differences of opinion as instanced by a paper on an astronomical topic, which Piazzi Smyth strongly recommended should be published while Professor Grant just as firmly advocated rejection. Council decided that publication was 'inexpedient'.

The early volumes of *Transactions* contained *Proceedings*, but in 1805 this practice lapsed and it was not until 1832 that *Proceedings* were again produced and appeared annually as separate publications. Until recently *Transactions* contained papers on an assortment of subjects including geology, biology and mathematics, while *Proceedings* in addition to shorter papers contained notices of meetings, Presidential Addresses, obituary notices, and other matters of interest. Both *Transactions* and *Proceedings* are still published (*vide infra*) and others have been added. *Communications* introduced in 1975 provides an outlet for publication in the physical sciences. Because of the existence of other specialised journals in this general area the publication may well have to be discontinued.

After many years of 'experimentation' the Society now produces regularly, in addition to the *Year Book*, three journals, each with its own Editorial Board (p. 136). All papers are submitted to independent referees for their opinion and guidance.

Transactions are now devoted entirely to the Earth Sciences. *Proceedings A* accepts papers in mathematics and *Proceedings B* publishes papers in the biological sciences in the widest sense from symposia or other meetings sponsored by the Society.

The Presidential Addresses and Obituary Notices in *Transactions* and *Proceedings* contain a fund of information about the Society and its history. Particularly worthy of mention are the addresses by J. D. Forbes (1862), Christison (1868), Brewster (1865), Moncreiff (1883), and Turner (1910) (see Bibliography, p. 157). Many of the obituary notices are models of their kind, informative and written in beautiful English. Of the earlier notices one may single out: John Playfair's notices of John Clerk of Eldin, James Hutton and Dr Matthew Stewart (*Trans.*, 1818–23, 9, 113; 1799–1803, 5, 39; 1783–85, 1, 57); Dugald Stewart on Adam Smith (*ibid.*, 1789–93, 3, 55); the Rev. Mr Archibald Alison (1757–1839) on Lord Woodhouselee (*ibid.*, 1815–18, 8, 515); Adam Ferguson on Joseph Black (*ibid.*, 1799–1803, 5, 101): and a 'charming biography' of Lord Abercromby (1745–95) by Henry Mackenzie (*Trans.*, 1793–97, 4, 1). In a different category is Piazzi Smyth's *éloge* of the astronomer Le Verrier (1811–77) (p. 25). Piazzi Smyth in turn presented some problems to his obituarist and the notice in *Proceedings* was discretion itself and merely referred to 'his published works on the Great Pyramid which have attracted much notice in this country and the United States' (p. 70). Not to mention Piazzi Smyth's contributions to astronomy and spectroscopy was surely an unforgiveable lapse, perhaps attributable to the fact that the oddities of a man can make such an impression that they obscure his more lasting qualities.

Of the papers which have appeared in *Transactions* five may be singled out: Hutton's 'Theory of the Earth' (p. 9), Graham's 'On the Law of Diffusion of Gases, (p. 79), Hope's 'Account of a Mineral from Strontian' (p. 78), and Kelvin's 'On the Dynamical Theory of Heat' and 'On a Universal Tendency in Nature to the Dissipation of Mechanical Energy' (p. 47). To these should perhaps be added Bayley Balfour's 'Botany of Socotra' (p. 77).

From the institution of the Society until 1970, Neill and Co. Ltd, Edinburgh, served as printers to the Society (p. 121).

Occasionally the Society sponsors the publication of books of special interest and importance (p. 27). Notable are the fifty volumes of the 'Challenger' reports (p. 114), but perhaps pride of place should go to *James Hutton's Theory of the Earth: The Lost Drawings*, published in 1978 by the Scottish Academic Press in association with the Society and the Geological Society of London. The drawings lay undisturbed for almost 200 years among the papers of the Clerks of Penicuik and came to light through the efforts of Sir John Clerk, Bart (F.R.S.E., 1977) and Dr C. D. Waterston. The volume contains facsimilies of drawings, made mostly by John Clerk of Eldin, which were intended to illustrate Hutton's famous 'Theory of the Earth' (p. 9) and is replete with interest with a text written by Professor G. Y. Craig (F.R.S.E., 1964), Professor D. B. McIntyre (F.R.S.E., 1953) and Dr C. D. Waterston (F.R.S.E., 1958). Publication was made possible by generous grants from the Carnegie Trust for the Universities of Scotland, the Russell Trust, the Geological Society of London and our Society. Professor Craig has pointed out that the Society in 1840 missed an opportunity of publishing the drawings (see D. Milne, *Trans.*, 1840, **14**, 295).

Other books sponsored by the Society include:

Memorial Volume of John Napier (edited by C. G. Knott) (p. 27)
Handbook of the Napier Celebrations (edited by E. M. Horsburgh, 1870–1935), 1914 (p. 27)
Collected Scientific Papers of John Aitken (edited by C. G. Knott for the R.S.E.) 1923, (p. 49)
James Gregory Tercentenary Volume (edited by Professor Herbert Westren Turnbull, 1885–1961), 1939.

The number of books written by Fellows, past and present, must be legion and some of them are mentioned in the text (e.g. pp. 46, 86, 89, 104). Many were doubtless written at a time when academic incomes were, to put it mildly, 'modest' and augmentation was welcome, but most were written because the authors felt they had something important to say, something which required integration in one or more volumes rather than having to be 'dug out' of scattered papers and reviews. Two books immediately come to mind. *An Enquiry into the Nature and Causes of the Wealth of Nations* by Adam Smith (1723–90), a Founder Member and a President of the Literary Class, has been described somewhat extravagantly as 'probably the most important book that has ever been written', but certainly was, as Sir Alexander Gray puts it, 'one of the major landmarks in the world's intellectual history'.[6] The second book, Charles Darwin's revolutionary *On the Origin of Species by Natural Selection* appeared eighty years later and is a classic in scientific literature (p. 29).

It is impossible to do justice to the many other books written by Fellows, but one or two may be singled out. Clerk Maxwell's *Electricity and Magnetism* (1873) has been described as 'one of the most splendid books ever written by a man of science' and one which 'must remain one of the supreme classics of mathematical physics', while the term classic has also been applied to the *Treatise on Natural Philosophy* by Tait and Thomson (p. 46). It is intriguing to note that Thomson at one point in his career somewhat scathingly likened the practice of writing scientific books to 'an army in which a general is employed in teaching the goose-step to recruits'. Tait held quite a different view on book writing and it was largely thanks to his dogged persistence that 'T and T''' (the nickname of the 'Treatise') saw the light of day.

Other books read by generations of students include James Walker's *Physical Chemistry*, James Geikie's *The Great Ice Age*, D'Arcy Thompson's *Growth and Form* (p. 104), Arthur Holmes' *Principles of Physical Geology* and Charles Lyell's *Principles of Geology* which ran to twelve editions.

Library

Our knowledge of the first ninety years of the Library is limited and uncertain, but it is known that in 1850 there were 5,000 volumes on the shelves. A year later Council debated the 'defective state of the Library' only to be informed some months later that 'the Library is now one of the best scientific libraries in the United Kingdom'. There certainly was a lack of adequate administration although the part-time Librarians did their best and in 1858 Mr Haig and Dr George Lawson produced a badly needed printed catalogue of the Society's books, maps and journals, an achievement testifying to the enthusiasm of these workers.

A great improvement was effected in 1876 with the appointment of Mr James Gordon as Librarian and the establishment of a Library Committee, whose Minute Book (1876–1934) contains a wealth of information. Claims that the Society now had a 'Reference Library of all scientific publications in the world' were probably justified and that '. . . the Library has been kept as a complete repertory of original sources of information in every branch of mathematical, physical and natural science' was evidenced by its use by contributors to one edition of the *Encyclopoedia Britannica*. No library, however, completely fulfills its purpose without the presence of a dedicated *full-time* Librarian who not only ensures that a regular programme of systematic purchasing, weeding-out, and gap-filling is carried out, but also acts as guide, philosopher and friend to all library users. It is certain that the Library suffered from the lack of such an appointment. One admirable feature of the Library must, however, be noted. It has always been the custom to make it accessible without fee to all literary and scientific workers who are qualified to make use of it.[7]

Over the years the Library increased enormously from 30,000 volumes in 1909 to 250,000 in 1975, mostly in the form of scientific journals. Until recently the Society owned long runs of important scientific journals as well as those of lesser known Societies, but was faced with a severe problem of accommodation as well as by the seemingly never ending proliferation of scientific journals. Finally Council, after years of discussion and consultation, decided to accept the Scottish Education Department's offer for the transfer of the Society's holdings of foreign periodicals to the National Library of Scotland in order to establish the nucleus of a Scottish Science Reference Library (p. 137).

A feature of the Society's Library was the great reliance placed on the exchange of the Society's publications with those of other learned bodies (p. 12). Some idea of the variety of these exchanges can be gathered from the Minute of one Library Committee meeting where it was decided to effect exchanges with the Imperial Meteorological Society of St Petersburg, the Bohemian Academy in Prague, the University of Chicago, the Scientific Society of Chile and the Reale Instituto d'Incorragiamenti of Naples. From time to time the Society has helped sister societies in trouble as, for instance, when it sent back-numbers of *Transactions* and *Proceedings* to replace those in the University of Strassburg whose library was destroyed by bombardment during the Franco–Prussian War.

The collection of monographs is valuable, although it is not always easy to understand the policy (if any) under which it has been compiled. Chance and circumstance have given rise to a rather haphazard collection in which books of importance find themselves alongside many of little interest and relevance. It may be added that the elements of surprise and charm are not lacking. For example, in the *Memoir of Edward Forbes* by George Wilson and Archibald Geikie are to be found inserted original pen sketches by Forbes, while Piazzi Smyth's hand-written note books contain many pleasant, rather quaint sketches in colour. Volumes of historical interest are: *Essays, Observations, Physical and Literary read before a Society in Edinburgh* (3 volumes, 1754, 1756, 1771) and *Medical Essays and Observations*, revised and published by a Society in Edinburgh (1733–44) (p. 2). Of particular interest to the Society is the copy of an autograph letter written by Colin Maclaurin on 7 June 1737 at Dean in which he describes the foundation of a Society for Improving Arts and Science and particularly Natural Knowledge (p. 19).

The Society owes a great debt to Professor David Hume (1757–1838), nephew of David Hume, for his gift of his uncle's letters and miscellaneous papers. The papers include the original manuscript of the earlier part of Hume's *History of England* which show how carefully he revised his compositions. The letters are comprised of 145 written by Hume and some 550 addressed to him. The value the Society attaches to the manuscripts is reflected in the conclusions of a committee set up in 1841 that 'the collection must inalienably remain in the Society' and that 'to convert it into pecuniary speculation would be an abuse of the confidence reposed in them by the testator'. The manuscripts have been intensively studied by many scholars.[8]

Finally may be noted the complete runs of the *Philosophical Transactions of the Royal Society of London* and of the Society's *Transactions, Proceedings, Communications* and *Year Book* not to mention the fifty volumes of the 'Challenger' Reports (*Report on the Scientific Results of the Voyage of H.M.S. Challenger during the years 1873–76*, London, Edinburgh and Dublin: H.M.S.O., 1880–95).

Among the oddities of the Library is the Minute Book of the Academy of Physics at Edinburgh covering the period 7 January 1797 to 10 February 1798. The Academy[9] which existed for three and a half years was founded largely at the instigation of Henry Brougham, later Lord Chancellor, and included Francis Horner (1778–1817), John Leyden and William Erskine in its membership. The formation of the Society can be traced to a number of causes including Brougham's strong aversion to the Royal Societies of London and Edinburgh: societies which as he wrote are 'sunk in a sort of inertia' and 'useless to science'. Rotheram and Leslie were obviously not the only ones to view the Society unfavourably (pp. 69, 70).

One of the most distinctive features of the academic scene in recent years has been the proliferation of scientific journals. Formerly research was covered to a considerable extent by the journals of the learned societies, but since World War II a host of specialised journals, many published by private firms, have come on the market and the Society found itself with neither the space nor the resources to maintain a comprehensive coverage of the world's publications in science and the arts. As already noted it was decided to dispose of a large portion of the Library to the Scottish Science Reference Library (S.S.R.L.) or by sale (see Chapter VII). The Society retains its own publications as well as those of the Royal Society of London and the Royal Irish Academy and special holdings such as those of Hume, Hutton and Piazzi Smyth, together with journals such as the *Edinburgh Review* which have close relevance to the history of the Society. A number of monographs written by or about Fellows of the Society will also be retained.

Notes

1   It is only fair to quote Scott's opinion of Williams 'whose extensive information, learning, and lively talent makes him always pleasant company'.

2   Henry Lonsdale, *A Sketch of the Life and Writings of Robert Knox, the Anatomist* (London, 1870). A. S. Currie, *Proc. Roy. Soc. Med.*, 1933, **26**, 39.

3   No mention of the incident is to be found in the Society's records.

4   The Society may have felt that some scientific topics were more fittingly introduced by other societies such as the Society of Arts for Scotland to which Andrew Fyfe (1792–1861), Professor of Medicine and Chemistry at Aberdeen University, read a lecture in 1839 with reference to Fox Talbot's work. One of the earliest reviews on photography was Brewster's 'On Photogenic Drawing' (*Edin. Rev.*, 1843, **76**, 309).

5   Another factor was the express wish of the Society not to publish papers of a purely critical nature (*Proc.*, 1868–69, **6**, 404).

6   In marked contrast Alexander Carlyle (1722–1805) found the book 'tedious and full of repetition'.

7   'The Council of the R.S.E. resolve that in accordance with long established practice the Society's Library be accessible without fee to all literary and scientific workers who are qualified to make use of it, and are introduced to the Librarian by a Fellow of the Society' (Council Minutes, 1 December 1919).

8   See Calendar of Hume manuscripts. J. Y. T. Greig and H. Benyon, *Proc.*, 1932, **52**, 1.

9   G. N. Cantor, *Social Stud. Sci.*, 1975, **5**, 109.

CHAPTER III

Sage Councillors

Institutions like this have usually advanced under the momentum of great personalities—personalities whose influence has persisted long after their own time.

Sir Edward Appleton[1]

A strong and representative Council, however essential for administration and development is not in itself sufficient to maintain and enhance the life and undertakings of the Society. This point was emphasised by Principal James D. Forbes (*Proc.*, 1862, 5, 2)[2]: 'Every associated body must receive its vigour from a few zealous and spirited individuals who find pleasure in that species of business, which, were it left to the care of its members in general, would be often reluctantly submitted to, and always negligently executed.' Kelland later pursued the same theme (*ibid.*, 1878–79, 10, 34): 'The vitality of a Society like ours is kept up by a few ardent spirits, whose contributions like the life blood trickle through the veins of the Society and warm and animate its remotest members.' The Society's achievements are therefore reflected in the lives of those 'zealous spirits' who devote many years of service to its cause and in whose lives the welfare of the Society plays an important part. In the following pages an outline, necessarily brief and selective, is given of the lives of those Fellows who have guided the Society during its 200 years of existence.

The Society owes a special debt to William Robertson (1721–93), Principal of the University of Edinburgh, who in 1782, convened a meeting of the professors of the University and proposed a scheme 'for the establishment of a New Society more widely based than the languishing Philosophical Society (of Edinburgh)' (p. 2). Doubtless Robertson had been encouraged by fellow members of the Philosophical Society to take such a step and Walker and Cullen in particular had made no secret of their desire to see formed 'an institution which will be of general utility and credit to the country'. As a result of the professorial deliberations the Philosophical Society was subsumed into the Royal Society of Edinburgh in 1783 (p. 4).

Robertson, a minister of the Church of Scotland, was notable as a historian, and it was said of him that 'he was not the greatest British historian of his time, but only because he was a contemporary of Edward Gibbon'. It is pleasing to note that Gibbon on the other hand stated: 'he was proud to be third in the triumvirate of historians—Roberston, Hume and himself'. Robertson was a leader of the intellectual life of Edinburgh at a time when the Senatus was composed of a body of famous men unequalled in any other university of the time (p. 7). Robertson's portrait by Raeburn hangs in the Old Senate Hall of Edinburgh University.

If the Society was fortunate in having a man of Robertson's standing at its institution it was doubly fortunate in having John Robison (1739–1805) as its first General Secretary (1783–98). Robison used his ten years in office to advantage and placed the Society on a sound administrative footing. On the recommendation of Robertson he was elected to the Chair of Natural Philosophy at the University by the Town Council without the Councillors knowing whether or not he would accept. James Watt said of him: 'He was a man of the clearest head and the most science I have ever known', and stated that it was Robison who first suggested to him the application of the power of the steam engine to move carriage wheels. Robison's contributions to knowledge include the invention of ball-headed magnets which have been much used in research, and a paper entitled 'The Motion of Light as affected by Refracting and Reflecting Substances, which are also in Motion' (*Trans.*, 1790, **2**, 83), which is a pioneer investigation leading to the theory of relativity. As a young man he had a varied career and on one occasion found himself as a midshipman at the Battle of Quebec in the same boat as General Wolfe. He heard the General recite Gray's 'Elegy' under the Heights of Abraham and add that he would prefer being the author of the poem to the glory of beating the French on the morrow.

Robison's son, Sir John Robison (1778–1843), like his father was an excellent General Secretary (1828–39). In a paper (*Trans.*,

1826–30, **11**, 345) he described a Timekeeper which was made in 1830 by William Whitelaw. The instrument has an escapement which requires no oil, a pendulum made of marble, and still keeps excellent time in the Society's House.

A leading figure in the Society was Sir Thomas Makdougall Brisbane (1773–1860) after whom the capital of Queensland is named, who was President of the Society for 28 years. He established a meteorological magnetic observatory at Makerstoun near Kelso (p. 101) under the direction of Allan Broun and the observations made there fill three volumes of *Transactions* (1845, **17**: 1848, **18**: 1849, **19**) with a supplement by Balfour Stewart (*ibid.*, 1861, **22**, 59). Broun published papers of importance on the diurnal variations of the magnetic declination, and demonstrated the connection between the appearance of sun spots and magnetic storms. Knott wrote: 'Broun of all Edinburgh's scientific sons has done more than any other single worker to bring to light the hidden mysteries of magnetic variation'. This subject was also studied by an Honorary Fellow, the gifted Johann von Lamont (1805–79), born John Lamont, who at the age of 17 left his native Deeside to further in Munich his studies in the Roman Catholic Church. In the event he spent much of his life as Professor of Astronomy at the University of Munich. Sun spots and their meteorological effects were also investigated by Balfour Stewart (p. 112) and still earlier, by one of the Founder Fellows of the Society, Alexander Wilson (1714–86), first Professor of Practical Astronomy in Glasgow, who postulated that: 'The spots are cavities or depressions in that immensely resplendent substance which invests the body of the sun'. Wilson, it may be mentioned improved thermometers by drawing the capillary bore in an elliptical form so that the mercury thread was more readily visible. These thermometers were used by Cullen and Black in their researches.

John Playfair (1748–1819) (p. 86), a man of great erudition and charm, was according to Lord Moncreiff 'for the first two decades of the Society the life and soul of that institution'. As General Secretary (1798–1819) he was responsible not only for the administration of the Society, but also for arranging and publishing the *Transactions* without much if any clerical assistance. He prophesised that it might be possible to illuminate the whole of Edinburgh with artificial light by means of 'inflammable air alone', an idea which was received by his friends with good natured derision.[3] Lord Lauderdale opined that this was 'rather a bold as well as novel experiment' to which Playfair replied that 'Experiments usually point at novelty, otherwise they can scarcely be so termed'. R. P. Gillies reports that Playfair dealt with this and other points with 'immutable good humour' and one can understand why Cockburn in his 'Memorials' refers to Playfair as that 'amiable philosopher'. Playfair's forecast was implemented when shortly afterwards William Murdoch showed that coal gas could be carried through pipes and used for artificial light.[4] Murdoch it may be noted was not a Fellow of the Society, but nevertheless his portrait hangs on the walls of 22 George Street.

Another of Hutton's disciples was Sir James Hall (1761–1832) who was President (1812–20) and was described by Lord Moncreiff as 'one of our most energetic members' (p. 86).

Bridging the interval between the brilliant era of Robertson, Black and Hutton and the golden years of Kelvin and Tait was Sir David Brewster (1781–1868), and it is difficult to exaggerate his devotion and service to the Society. He surely was the 'noblest Roman of them all'. He read his first paper to the Society in 1810 and for a period of nearly 60 years until his death enriched it with numerous papers in *Transactions* and *Proceedings*. He published 381 papers, evidence of great industry although very many fewer than the 967 credited in the Royal Society of London lists to Arthur Cayley (1821–95; Hon. F.R.S.E., 1865). His researches covered almost every branch of optics including the law of polarisation of light, double refraction and biaxial crystals, and Sir George Airy (1801–92; Hon. F.R.S.E., 1835) called him the 'father of modern experimental optics'. He invented the kaleidoscope and patented it, but the invention was pirated by others and Brewster made not a penny by it. In the event he died a comparatively poor man. More importantly, in 1811, Brewster invented the dioptric lens (*Trans.*, 1826, **11**, 33) and realised its importance in lighthouse illumination since his lens system concentrated all the light from a lamp into one wide and parallel beam. In spite of every effort on his part, the United Kingdom lighthouse authorities refused to use the invention. To his chagrin, eleven years later, Fresnel had the same idea and succeeded in getting it adopted in French lighthouses, and Brewster had to wait until 1835 when his dioptric apparatus was installed in the Inchkeith lighthouse and subsequently in all new lighthouses. Brewster attributed his own failure to the fact that on the British lighthouse boards there was not a scientific officer or adviser with any knowledge of optics. Many of the improvements later effected by the Stevensons (p. 83) were modifications of Brewster's ideas.

Brewster was twice Keith Prizeman and like Faraday was the recipient of the Copley, Rumford and Royal Medals from the Royal Society of London. In spite of his many commitments he found time to be General Secretary (1819–28) and President of the Society (1864–68). On 21 February 1831 he wrote to Charles Babbage (1792–1871) asking what he thought of the possible founding of an Association in the United Kingdom similar to that of the German Naturalists and the idea was adopted with alacrity and resulted in the first meeting of the British Association for the Advancement of Science being held later in the year in York. The 'soul of the meeting' according to Brewster was the Rev. William Vernon Harcourt, who was ably assisted by Brewster, Sir John Robison, James D. Forbes, J. F. W. Johnston and others.

It is perhaps surprising that Brewster never occupied a university chair, although thanks to the good offices of that odd character, the Earl of Buchan (p. 3), he was offered one at the Russian University of Vilna. Whether his somewhat sour observation that the work of professorships is fatal to original investigation was the cause or effect of lack of a professorial post it is difficult to say. Nevertheless he was the first physicist to become head of a British University when he was appointed Principal of St Andrews University (1838–59). Later at the advanced age of 78 he became Principal of Edinburgh University (1859–68).

Brewster was a strong personality, high spirited and excitable, who according to Lyon Playfair 'little understood the art of compromise and sometimes found himself involved in time-wasting petty disputes'. It is only fair to record that Brewster's outspokenness was sometimes not without justification as witness his crusade, vigorous if over-zealous, against long standing abuses —the 'cosy jobbery' in Douglas Young's words—in St Andrews University, which he succeeded in eradicating.[5] It is pleasant to record that he mellowed with age and his final years were characterised by 'unimpaired cordiality'. Even in his earlier years, however, Brewster could face difficulty and disappointment with dignity and equanimity. In 1833 both he and James D. Forbes were candidates for the Chair of Natural Philosophy at Edinburgh and Lord Neaves was later able to write: 'It is creditable to both parties and more especially to Sir David Brewster, that the contests thus terminated (in the appointment of Forbes) did not dissolve their friendship or prevent their cordial co-operation in everything that could promote the interests of science'.

Recognition of Brewster's achievements as physicist, administrator, scientific journalist, historian, churchman and a founder of the British Association was evidenced by a symposium held on 21 November 1981 and organised by four scientific bodies including the Society to commemorate the bicentenary of Brewster's birth.

'Indefatigable in attention to the welfare of the Royal Society of Edinburgh of which he was General Secretary for twenty years' was James David Forbes (1809–68).[6] He was the son of the famous banker, Sir William Forbes, and of his wife, Williamina Belsches, Scott's first love. Like Clerk Maxwell he was an infant prodigy and as a boy he frequently attended meetings of the Society. Brewster proposed him for Fellowship in 1829, but the proposal was turned down on account of Forbes being 'under age', an odd decision since Sir George Stewart Mackenzie (1780–1848) was elected in 1799, having just celebrated his nineteenth birthday. Forbes was, however, elected age 21 in 1831 and except for Stewart Mackenzie he, Thomas Graham and Maclagan Wedderburn are the youngest Fellows ever to be elected (pp. 79, 94). Self-educated in his younger days, except for some tuition from the local dominie, Forbes held the Chair of Natural Philosophy in the University of Edinburgh (1833–60) before becoming Principal of St Andrews University. He discovered the polarisation of heat, an important contribution to the undulatory theory of heat (*Trans.*, 1833–36, **13**, 446; 1836–40, **14**, 176) and published many papers on geology, especially on the nature and flow of glaciers (p. 69). His papers to the Society were stated to 'shed a new lustre upon the transactions of that body'. Ill health forced him to decline the Presidency offered to him shortly before his death.

Another devoted servant of the Society was Peter Guthrie Tait (1831–1901), Professor of Natural Philosophy at the University of Edinburgh (1860–1901). He was a classmate of Fleeming Jenkin and junior to Clerk Maxwell by one year at Edinburgh

Academy (p. 103) and was elected to the Fellowship in 1860. A regular attender at the Society's meetings he served on Council in one capacity or another for 39 years (1862–1901), and frequently made communications on physical and mathematical problems. Most of his papers were published by the Society and *Transactions* and *Proceedings* were Tait's favourite *media* of publication. Cargill Knott states that in the seventies and eighties 'Tait was in fact the Royal Society [of Edinburgh]' and it was there that he frequently met Kelvin and formed with him a most productive association (p. 35). The two played a great role in maintaining the prestige of the Society and their book *Treatise on Natural Philosophy* was said by Max Born to be a 'sort of Bible of mathematical science to us'. According to Knott its publication was 'an event of the first importance'. A somewhat different assessment was given by J. M. Barrie in his *Edinburgh Eleven* when he called the abridged version of the book 'The Student's first Glimpse of Hades'.

Tait's researches covered a number of topics including the conductivity of heat, thermoelectricity and the kinetic theory of gases. Four papers on the last-named subject are to be found in *Transactions*, 1885–87, **33**, 65, 251; 1887–89, **35**, 1029; 1889–91, **36**, 257. In all Tait published 365 papers, and a facsimile of notes written two days before he died is to be found in *Proceedings*, 1901–02, **24**, 344.

Tait never became a Fellow of the Royal Society of London, maintaining that when he was young he coveted the honour but could not afford it and when he could afford it he had ceased to desire the distinction. According to Cargill Knott, about 1880 the President of the Royal Society of London suggested privately to Tait that he allow his name to go forward to that Society's Council, but Tait, who knew that the name of a valued friend had recently been rejected by Council replied that he had no pretensions to belong to a Society which was too good for his friend. This reply served not only its immediate purpose, but also to Tait's delight helped to procure for his friend soon afterwards the distinction he sought.

Tait was a keen golfer, playing on Bruntsfield Links and on holiday at St Andrews, where at one period he frequently played five rounds a day. A 6.30 a.m. start was necessary for such adventures and it is said that he did two rounds before breakfast at

William Robertson

Henry, Duke of Buccleuch

John Robison

James Hutton

Sir Walter Scott

James Clerk Maxwell (with his mother)

Lord Kelvin

P. Guthrie Tait

10 a.m. The famous story that on 11 January 1893 his son, Freddie Tait, the amateur champion, had a great drive of 250 yards and thereby proved his father's calculations to be erroneous, is unfortunately not true. Tait in fact never 'made any rash statement as to the greatest possible distance attainable by a well-driven ball' (Cargill Knott).

Tait enjoyed the assistance in his researches of many young men who had no intention of undertaking a scientific career and somewhat unexpectedly Robert Louis Stevenson was one of these. R.L.S., at his father's wish, worked for a short time in Tait's laboratory, but experience did nothing to interest him in science. He did, however, contribute a rather dull paper to the Society on a forestry topic (*Proc.*, 1872–73, **8**, 114). Much more lively and in places moving are his 'Memoir of Fleeming Jenkin' and an essay on his father, Thomas Stevenson. In *Some College Memories* he recalls with affection Tait and his assistant Thomas Lindsay, as well as Kelland, Chrystal and Blackie, while in *Virginibus Puerisque* he describes John Clerk of Eldin 'who with playing pieces of cork on his own dining table invented modern naval warfare'.

Sir William Thomson, later Lord Kelvin (1824–1907), like James D. Forbes and Clerk Maxwell, early displayed his exceptional intellectual gifts by entering the University of Glasgow at the age of ten and publishing a paper on Fourier's Theory when he was 17. He became a Fellow of the Society in 1847 and many of his papers containing his most brilliant investigations and discoveries were published in the Society's *Transactions* and *Proceedings*. He published his epoch-making series of articles on thermodynamics in the years 1851–54, a period which included the reconciliation of Joule's and Carnot's principles (*Trans.*, 1851, **20**, 261, 289). In one paper 'On a Universal Tendency in Nature to the Dissipation of Mechanical Energy' (*Proc.*, 1852, **3**, 139) Kelvin arrived at the remarkable conclusion that 'within a finite period of time past the earth must have been and within a finite period of time to come must again be unfit for the habitation of man as at present constituted'. In other publications he described his hydrodynamic investigations and his researches on the refraction and diffraction of light. His last paper in *Proceedings* appeared a year before he died.[7] Kelvin is one of the great figures of science and as Sir Alfred Ewing stated: 'No other contributor has done so much to give our publications a world-wide and

47

lasting fame'. The esteem in which he was held is testified by his 21 years as President of the Society (p. 13).

A greatly respected Fellow—'our dear friend and colleague' according to William Turner—was Alexander Crum Brown (1838–1922), half-brother of Dr John Brown of 'Rab and his Friends' fame, who was a Secretary to Ordinary Meetings for 26 years and his services to the Society in this capacity, as a Member of Council, or as Vice-President were spread over a record period of 44 years (p. 80). He published most of his papers in *Transactions* or *Proceedings* and this was felt by some to have prevented his researches receiving the recognition they merited since these journals were not always accessible to chemists.

In 1901 on the death of Tait, George Chrystal (1851–1912), Professor of Mathematics at Edinburgh University, was appointed General Secretary, but he can have had no inkling of the magnitude of the task which lay ahead. The Society had been one of the bodies which proposed the erection of the Royal Institution (p. 19) and had been for eighty years one of the tenants therein. It is not surprising that the Society had come to regard the Institution as its permanent home and indeed in 1903 suggested on the initiative of John Murray that it be devoted entirely to science. It therefore came as a shock when in 1906 the Society learned that the Government intended it to be used to promote the Fine Arts and become one of the National Galleries of Scotland.[8] The Society thus found itself without a home and a request to the Secretary for Scotland for recognition of the Society and its needs brought only the unsatisfactory reply that 'it was not supported by the body of public opinion'. Fortunately, greater success attended the subsequent negotiations (p. 6) in which Lord Kelvin and Sir William Turner played an important role. No less important was the energetic lobbying of Members of Parliament in London by Noel Paton (1859–1928), Professor of Physiology in Glasgow University, and Chrystal's diligence and unrivalled knowledge of the Society's history and affairs. Chrystal and Turner must have looked back on the opening of the rooms in George Street on 8 November 1909 with great satisfaction, for, to use Sir William Turner's words: 'no longer were we tenants-at-will of apartments to be disposed of at short notice: we sit rent free in a handsome and commodious building with the occupancy ensured by a Parliamentary title'. It was Chrystal who ascertained that the present rooms in George Street could be purchased, and it was Turner who so persuaded the Secretary for Scotland, Lord Pentland, that the Treasury granted the necessary £25,000 for the purchase of 22–24 George Street and £3,000 to cover the cost of removal and equipment. As John Horne stated in *The Student* (11 July 1916): 'The present rooms may not inaptly be regarded as a monument to two distinguished men', Chrystal and Turner. A feature of the negotiations, it is pleasant to add, was the courteous language used by both sides in all the correspondence.

One of the great General Secretaries of the Society was Cargill G. Knott (1856–1922), who by both written word and deed succeeded in enhancing the reputation of the Society at home and abroad. He was a physicist and mathematician who entered Tait's laboratory in 1873 and for many years afterwards was a member of the Department of Natural Philosophy at Edinburgh University. Doubtless he derived some of his enthusiasm for the Society from Tait and from 1894 was a Member of Council and from 1911 until his death General Secretary. His life was one of unobtrusive diligence and he not only contributed fifty papers to *Proceedings*, but also edited a *Napier Tercentenary Memorial Volume* and another volume containing the *Collected Scientific Papers of John Aitken LL.D., F.R.S.* (p. 34). His *magnum opus* was his book *Life and Collected Papers of Peter Guthrie Tait*, which was reckoned by Whittaker to be 'one of the best scientific biographies ever written', high praise from such a fastidious critic. He contributed authoritative articles to the *Encyclopaedia Britannica* and *Chamber's Encyclopaedia* and with A. Yule Fraser and A. J. G. Barclay of George Watson's Boys' College founded the Edinburgh Mathematical Society.

Knott had the gift of narrative and he leaves us with an unforgettable picture of the Society in the vintage years at the end of the last century. 'It seems but yesterday when Piazzi Smyth with the peculiar hesitation in his speech, uttered the *éloge* of Le Verrier in the quaint-wrought involved sentences of a by-gone century. Or it was Kelvin moving eagerly on the soft carpet, and putting his gyroscopes through their dynamical drill: or Fleeming Jenkin amusing and instructing the audience with the sound of the first phonograph, as he used it to analyse human speech: or Lister quaffing a glass of milk which had stood for weeks under a

49

light stopper which no germs could creep through: or Turner demonstrating whales' bones or human skulls: Tait himself talking, in easy words, about strains and mirages, the kinetic theory of gases, or the spin of golf balls'. This agrees with the picture painted by Sir Alfred Ewing who recollected that as a boy he attended meetings of the Society to 'watch the play of the great giants of these days, men like Sir William Thomson (later Lord Kelvin), Tait, Lister and Turner'. An earlier unsolicited testimonial came in 1865 from Clerk Maxwell who regarded the Society as a 'very sociable body, most of them good speakers as well as sensible men'. It is clear from other evidence, however, that certain periods in the history of the Society lacked the verve and vitality of the Kelvin-Tait period.[9]

In recent times no one has promoted the interests of the Society more than Professor James P. Kendall (1889–1978), who served on Council for 23 years, finally as President (1949–54), the first chemist to hold this office. During his time as General Secretary Kendall was responsible for several developments. He replaced the highly specialised papers read at meetings by addresses of a more general type on carefully selected topics and this move proved to be highly successful (p. 24). He was also responsible for inaugurating the scheme for administration of the Robert Cormack Bequest by the Society and for placing the Alembic Club under the *aegis* of the Society. Finally it was during his period of office that women were admitted to the Society's Fellowship. Until then the R.S.E. was a man's Society with women sometimes barred from its conversaziones and permitted to use the Library only after permission had been granted by Council. In 1941 Dr Lancelot Hogben (1895–1975) proposed that Council should approve membership of women suitably qualified, but nothing was done to implement this until in 1949 Dr (later Professor) Charlotte Auerbach, Dr Ethel Dobbie Currie, Dr Sheina Macalister Marshall, Dr Christina C. Miller and Dr Doris L. Reynolds were elected Fellows and signed the Roll Book. Dr Marshall had accompanied Professor (later Sir) Maurice Yonge on his 1928 Great Barrier Reef Expedition (p. 103). Dr Miller (1927–29) and Dr Auerbach (1945–47) were recipients of the Keith Prize, and Dr Currie (1943–45) and Dr Marshall (1969–71) received the Neill Prize. Clearly the advent of the distaff side added distinction to the Society.[10]

Inspection of the names on pp. 161–163 demonstrates beyond doubt that the Society has always enjoyed the services of distinguished men of eminence as Presidents and General Secretaries of the Society. It must be conceded that the first President, Henry Scott, 3rd Duke of Buccleuch, although he was President for twenty-nine years, attended meetings of the Society very rarely and Scott, though conscientiously chairing meetings of the Society and the Council whenever possible, took little part in the day to day running of the Society. In fact it was not until the 1860s when David Brewster was elected that the Presidency involved active participation in the Society's administration. Brewster's successors have followed his good example and without exception have devoted time and energy to the Society's affairs. Special mention must be made of Lord Kelvin who played such a crucial role at a very critical moment in the Society's existence (p. 48). The last twenty years have seen ever increasing demands on our Presidents.

From the beginning the Society's success has depended to a great extent on the dedication and efficiency of the General Secretaries and it is difficult to exaggerate the debt the Society owes to the sixteen men, all academics with the exception of Sir John Robison, who have in Scriptural terms 'borne the burden and heat of the day'. Forbes (*Proc.*, 1844–45, **2**, 68) said of Sir John that 'he always attached himself to the concern of our Society as his chief and main occupation'. Without fear of contradiction the same can be said of all Sir John's predecessors and successors in their role as General Secretaries. The Society's Fellows should indeed be grateful that men of calibre are willing to devote their selfless services for the well-being of the Society. Particularly heavy responsibilities must have lain on the shoulders of the early General Secretaries and later General Secretaries on occasion have been called to deal with situations they little anticipated (see, e.g. p. 48). The last twenty years have witnessed great changes in the Society's activities and the transfer of the Library to the National Library and the rehabilitation of the George Street rooms have made quite exceptional demands on the Secretaries of the period.

There is no doubt that the Society continues to enjoy the zeal and dedication of men of eminence who function as Officers. Among those who have served in one capacity or another a few may be mentioned: Professor R. A. Sampson (1866–1939;

General Secretary, 1923–33), Professor Norman Feather (1904–78; General Secretary, 1956–66; President 1967–70), Lord Balerno (F.R.S.E., 1928; Treasurer, 1967–77), Professor James Ritchie (1882–1958; President, 1954–58) (p. 104) and his son Dr Anthony Ritchie who served on Council for 22 years including ten as General Secretary. The services of the Ritchies recall those of John Robison (p. 41) and his son Sir John Robison (p. 41). Special mention must be made of Professor Norman Davidson (1911–72), who in spite of recurrent illness devoted much time and thought to the Society and very generously presented a medallion to be worn by the President on appropriate ceremonial occasions. The President's desire that the medallion should incorporate the Society's Arms led to the unexpected discovery that the Arms used by the Society for some 150 years were in fact illegal.[11] Norman Davidson immediately enlisted the help of Stanley Cursiter (1887–1976) and held discussions with Sir Thomas Innes of Learney, Lord Lyon King of Arms, and as a result the Society in June 1967 received Letters Patent giving it recognised Armorial Bearings, Incorporating a Canton with the Royal Arms of Scotland. Perhaps the most unusual feature of the Shield is the intertwining lines representing the DNA Double Helix, symbolising the growth and advance of science and indicative of the President's particular research interest. The President's Medallion incorporates the Society's Arms.

Council

Members of Council will be the first to admit that their duties are lightened by the simple and workable Constitution under which they function, and it is significant that the composition of Council at the present day closely resembles that laid down in the original Laws of the Society. Length of service was then unspecified as is instanced by the first four General Secretaries—John Robison, John Playfair, David Brewster and Sir John Robison—holding office for a total of 56 years (1783–1839), while in the period 1840–1901 the post was held by three Fellows—James D. Forbes, John Hutton Balfour and Peter G. Tait (p. 45). No one can doubt the invaluable service by all these men, but in 1924 it was agreed that all Members of Council could serve in any one capacity for only a limited number of years:

President	Not exceeding 5 years
Vice-Presidents (6)	3
Secretaries to the Ordinary Meetings (2)	5
General Secretary	10
Treasurer	10
Curator of the Library and Museum	10
Councillors (12)	3

Previous to 1924 a number of modifications had been made from time to time, but these no longer obtain. It was decided, for example, that Presidents on retirement should become Honorary Vice-Presidents and that Council should include Past Presidents (*Proc.*, 1878, 10, 408), but implementation seems to have been of short duration.

In the original Laws the function and powers of Council were tersely described by the phrase 'the regulation of the private business of the Society' and the duties of Officers were described in a few lines (*Trans.*, 1804–11, 6, 5). It has to be admitted that the instructions were not always fully obeyed. The General Secretaries, for instance, were instructed to keep a Minute Book in which a *full* account of the proceedings of the Ordinary Meetings was given, but examination of the early Minute Books shows them to be woefully inadequate as records. The ambiguity of the powers of Council was also regrettable and gave rise on at least one occasion to unnecessary unpleasantness (p. 69). As happens, however, with most well run institutions the Society has seldom been dependent on reference to the Constitution but has relied largely on the good will and common sense of its Fellowship. It is nonetheless satisfactory that in the present-day Laws the duties and responsibilities of Council are clearly stated.

The method of electing Council is perhaps not entirely democratic, but it seems to be effective. Before each Statutory General Meeting Council submits and recommends to the Fellowship the names of Fellows to act as Officers and Members of Council for the ensuing session. Fellows can either approve or delete names and substitute other names, but invariably the Fellowship has accepted Council's nominations.

Administrative Staff

The original Laws made little provision for a permanent administrative staff beyond empowering the General Secretary 'to employ a clerk, to be paid by the Society'. Little is known about the implementation of this authorisation, but it is certain that in the early days the General Secretaries had to bear a heavy administrative load with little clerical assistance. Since the General Secretaries also acted as Editors of *Transactions* and *Proceedings* it is surprising that it was not until 1876 that the appointment of a permanent official was discussed. Previous to this the Society had for 43 years enjoyed the services of a 'meritorious House Officer', Mr Cockburn, who decided on account of old age and ill-health to retire in that year on a pension from the Society. Mr Cockburn had been a general utility officer, looking after the premises, receiving the annual subscriptions of Fellows, etc. At the same time a succession of men acted in a part-time capacity under a variety of titles such as Assistant Librarian or Treasurer's Clerk some of whom made useful contributions to the Society's welfare. Mr J. D. Haig and Dr George Lawson, for example, are specially mentioned in Council Minutes for compiling a catalogue of books in the Library. On Mr Cockburn's retirement Council felt that the time had come for the appointment of a qualified librarian whose duties would include, in addition to the supervision of the library, others such as assisting the General Secretary, collecting subscriptions, arranging the hall for meetings, and appointed Mr James Gordon, an Assistant in the University Library, at a salary of £120 per annum. The full-time appointment was a great success and Mr Gordon, noted for his 'unfailing and fine courtesy of manner' served the Society most loyally. According to D'Arcy Thompson, Mr Gordon in addition to his other gifts 'wrote to perfection the fluent, sonorous latin of the cosmopolitan Scholar. He loved to write [in latin] addresses for the Society to convey greetings to a foreign university or society'.

Mr Gordon on his retirement in March 1902 was succeeded by the Assistant Librarian, Mr John Hardy, who carried on the good work of his predecessor. He died in 1909 and his place was taken by Mr George Alexander Stewart (1885–1958), first as Interim Librarian and then as Librarian. Later the title was changed to that of Assistant Secretary and Librarian. Mr Stewart served the Society for more than fifty years under 12 Presidents and 6 General Secretaries from whom in his own words 'he received nothing but the greatest good will'. The Society showed their appreciation of Mr Stewart's services by electing him to the

Fellowship, a gesture which gave him great joy. He delighted in recalling the 'good old days' and in a few words could convey the excitement and liveliness of the meetings at the beginning of the century, often with Boswellian incisiveness. One example may be given. 'I well remember Lord Kelvin as President. He frequently came through from Glasgow to preside at Meetings of the Society, which were held at first at 8 p.m. and later in the afternoons at 4.30 p.m. I can recall Professor Crum Brown, on occasion, patiently waiting to take Lord Kelvin home from an evening Meeting with him, while his Lordship, Professor Chrystal and other distinguished physicists and mathematicians, with no thought of time, discussed some abstract problem in Physics and Mathematics'.

Mr Stewart often expressed the great assistance he received from Mr W. H. Rutherford, Assistant Librarian, and on his retirement Mr Rutherford was appointed to succeed him. In due course Mr Rutherford's title was changed to that of Executive Secretary and Librarian (1974). In 1973 he, like Mr Stewart, had been elected to Fellowship of the Society in recognition of his sterling and dedicated work.

Space forbids mention of other assistants who have helped the Society so cheerfully and efficiently. Professor Kendall on one occasion compared the permanent officials of the Society to the British civil servants 'whose experience is invaluable in moulding the crude ideas of cabinet ministers into workable shapes'. The Society certainly has every reason to be grateful to the 'supreme Permanent Officials' who have served it so well.

Notes

1 *Year Book*, 1962, p. 65.
2 Here Forbes is quoting word for word a statement to be found in the first volume of *Transactions*.
3 Among others who scorned the possibility of gas lighting were Humphry Davy, William Wollaston and Sydney Smith. Was it Sydney who said: 'one might as well try to light London with a slice of the moon'?
4 William Murdoch (p. 43) was the first to contemplate carrying gas through pipes and using it for artificial lighting and it is difficult to gainsay his modest statement: 'I believe, I may without presuming too much, claim both the idea of applying, and the first actual application of this gas to economical purposes' (*Phil. Trans. Roy. Soc. Lond.*, 1802, 98, 124. *Edinb. Rev.*, 1809, 13, 477). Andrew Ure lit his lecture theatre with

coal gas in 1805, the first gas light seen in Glasgow. Moncreiff in his Presidential Address (*Proc.*, 1882–84, **12**, 453) referred to the benefits derived from the replacement of candle light by the illumination of cities by gas.

5 'Sir David [Brewster] had no toleration for evils which it was in his power to redress and he set himself at once with his characteristic ardour and energy (not always tempered by prudence and patience) to abolish sinecures, to recover lost bursaries, and to exterpate the whole mass of time-honoured abuses which the indolence and neglect of his predecessors had allowed to accumulate in that ancient city of learning [St Andrews]'. (The Rev. James Taylor in Mrs Gordon's *Life of Brewster*). Scott in a letter wrote: '. . . though St. Andrews still as Johnson said *gets rich by degrees*'.

6 Forbes' influence is still felt for it was he who in 1845 initiated the practice of the General Secretary presenting his Report at the Statutory General Meetings of the Society.

7 Other Fellows who retained their mental vigour into old age include Brewster who worked to the last day of his life, Tait (p. 45) and Whittaker (p. 93). Two Fellows who have paid no heed to the warning of the Psalmist to those 'who by reason of strength be fourscore years' and continue their life work with unabated zest are Lord Cameron and Sir Maurice Yonge.

Some Fellows exhibited remarkable physical prowess after reaching their four score years. Andrew Duncan *senior* in his 83rd year climbed Arthur Seat on 1 May (1877) as he had done for 50 years, while Sir Richard Griffith at the age of 80 walked 18 miles in a day. At the same age Christison climbed Ben Vrackie and Robert Brown, aged 83, climbed Lochnagar. More recently C. T. R. Wilson in his eighties climbed Goat Fell leaving his younger companions panting behind.

8 For details see Report by Council to a General Meeting of the Society, 21 December 1906, also *Proceedings*, 1911, **32**, 498. By 1906 the R.S.E. were the only tenants in the Royal Institution, the Society for the Promotion of the Fine Arts having died many years previously and the Society of Antiquaries having left in 1892. See also Turner, *Transactions*, General Index, 1889–1908, p. 2.

9 See, e.g. Christison (*Proc.*, 1857–63, **4**, 4): 'I will not pretend to inquire into the causes which, for a few years past, have somehow or other lessened the interest of the meetings of the Society, in face of such ample resources'. The first volume of *Transactions* contains the prescient observation that 'Institutions of this kind have their intervals of langour as well as periods of brilliancy and activity.'

10 Earlier, ladies had read papers to the Society. One of the earliest was given on 3 June 1918, by Miss L. H. Huie.

It must be pointed out that the Laws of the Society indicated but did not specifically state that Fellowship be confined to the male sex.

11 In 1820 the Society approved and adopted a design for the Society's seal by James Skene of Rubislaw and this was used on the Society's documents and notepaper until 1966.

CHAPTER IV

Amateurs and their Achievements

The Fellowship should be open not only to those professionally engaged in scholarship and enquiry, but also to *mere amateurs* who are interested in instructing themselves in literature and science.

James D. Forbes

From the earliest days of its existence the Society has welcomed to its Fellowship amateurs or laymen who do not make a living from the cultivation or teaching of science[1] (p. 14): men and women who cultivate a subject as a pastime from sheer love and the interest it affords. The word amateur, it is true, is sometimes used in a disparaging sense, but it is the glory of the Society that it provides a forum for both the professional and the amateur thus enabling both to make valuable contributions to research and scholarship. In the following pages some of the achievements of the amateur are outlined.

Fellows whose independent means afforded them the leisure to pursue their scientific interests include giants such as James Hutton, Sir James Hall and Charles Darwin. Of Sir Roderick Murchison's amateur status there can be no doubt for when elected to Fellowship of the Royal Society of London in 1826 he was informed by his friend Sir Humphry Davy that the honour was bestowed because Sir Roderick was an independent gentleman having a taste for science and plenty of time and sufficient means to gratify it. In the same vein Sir Douglas Maclagan said of David Milne Home that 'he provided an admirable example of what may be done for science by a country gentleman possessed of means and leisure, but animated by the laudable ambition to extend the knowledge of his fellow men'. More modest were the claims of some of Tait's senior students who had no intention of becoming professional scientists, but who carried out scientific investigations in his laboratory (see, e.g. *Proc.*, 1869–72, **7**, 206). Illuminating too is Tait's remark: 'Mr George Barclay (1820–1910) is *not* a man of science: he is a man *intelligently interested* in science'. Tait showed his regard for this highly respected Fellow and businessman by dedicating to him his book *Recent Advances in Physical Science*.

The achievements of Hutton, Hall and other amateurs of similar calibre are mentioned in other parts of the book. This chapter is mainly concerned with those amateurs who have used their spare time in contributing significantly to the Society's meetings and publications. From the records it appears that geology is the science which has the greatest appeal to amateurs in the Fellowship. One of these was James Skene of Rubislaw (1775–1864), one of Scott's closest friends and advocate, geologist, archaeologist and artist. Another was Sir John H. S. Forbes (1804–66), one of the Founders of the Meteorological Society of Scotland, who acquired a taste for science at Edinburgh University and was specially interested in geology and meteorology. A well known enthusiast was Charles MacLaren (1782–1866), who wrote *The Geology of Fife and the Lothians*, contributed scientific articles to the *Encyclopaedia Britannica* and *The Scotsman*, and was editor of that paper. Some years previously in 1818, Robert Stevenson had suggested that passengers might be conveyed by railway and MacLaren took the matter a stage further by predicting that the speed of rail travel might reach 24 m.p.h. Less optimistic was the *Edinburgh Review*'s statement that the Atlantic would never be crossed by steam navigation.

A geologist with one of the finest mineralogical collections in Scotland was Thomas Allan (1777–1833), a banker who was a 'live-wire' in Edinburgh's intellectual circles and Keeper of the Society's Museum as well as Honorary Treasurer. The mineral *allanite* is named after him (*Trans.*, 1812, **6**, 371). The same distinction applies to Lord Greenock (1783–1859), who discovered the rare mineral *greenockite* (cadmium sulphide) near Port Glasgow (*Trans.*, 1838–40, **14**, 619). He was a Vice-President and it is recorded that 'his continuous interest in the Royal Society of Edinburgh formed an essential element in its prosperity'. Other minerals which have been named after Fellows are *hopeite* (*ibid.*, 1823–26, **10**, 107), *jamesonite*, and *brewsterite* (also known as *dysclasite*, *ibid.*, 1836, **13**, 46).

An outstanding amateur was Robert Chambers (1802–71) who, with his brother William (1800–83), founded the well-known publishing firm of W. and R. Chambers Ltd. Robert was self taught and became very interested in geology as is evidenced by the active part he took in discussions at the Society's meetings and by his paper 'On Glacial Phenomena in Peebles and Selkirk Shires' (*Proc.*, 1855, **3**, 308). He was the author of a famous and controversial book *Vestiges of the Natural History of Creation* (1844),[2] which boldly attacked the theology of the Creation. It ran to eleven editions and encountered much severe criticism, some of it undeserved. Murchison was a harsh critic, but Charles Darwin,[3] after reading the 10th edition (1853), praised its 'powerful and brilliant style' though regretting 'the lack of accurate knowledge and a great want of scientific caution'. None the less, he considered the book provided 'a valuable service in calling attention to the subject'. A recent facsimile reprint of the book entitled *Just before Darwin. Robert Chambers and the Vestiges* testifies to the interest it still provokes.[4]

Darwin was also critical of the work of David Milne, later David Milne Home (1805–90), but in the end generously acknowledged defeat. Milne, an advocate and country gentleman, interested in geology and meteorology suggested to James D. Forbes the invention of an instrument for detecting earthquakes and gave it the name *seismometer*, now generally known as a *seismograph*. Forbes duly obliged and invented the first scientific seismograph (*Trans.*, 1842, **15**, 219). J. A. (afterwards Sir Alfred) Ewing some forty years later invented the continuous seismograph.

In the present century amateurs have continued to contribute to the Society's activities. James Wright (1878–1957), a Kirkcaldy businessman and a life-long enthusiastic geologist and palaeontologist, became a leading authority on *Crinoidea* and in a long paper (*Trans.*, 1939–40, **60**, 1) summarised his activities over a period of forty years in systematically collecting crinoids. He was awarded the Neill Prize (1937–39) as well as the Worth Prize (1955), which is expressly devoted to the 'encouragement of amateur geological research'. More recently A. G. Long (F.R.S.E., 1962) gained the Makdougall–Brisbane Prize (1958–60) for his papers in *Transactions* on palaeobotany.

Mathematics too has attracted the attention of the Society's amateurs. Tait on one occasion (*Proc.*, 1871–72, **7**, 544) brought to the notice of the Society the names of three amateur mathematicians of special merit: William Archibald Cadell (1775–1855), Alexander Christison (1753–1820) and Lord Glenlee (1755–1846). Cadell's standing is shown by the special permission given to him by the French authorities to study in Paris during the Napoleonic wars, free from fear of internment or imprisonment. This recalls Humphry Davy's travels in 1813 by special permission of Napoleon. He was greeted with cordiality by *savants* such as Cuvier and von Humboldt and was entertained to dinner by the Société Philomathique. Christison, Professor of Latin in Edinburgh University and father of Robert Christison (p. 98), took up mathematical studies as a relaxation from his professional work and was described as 'one of the most profound amateur mathematicians in Scotland'. Lord Glenlee, son of the Chairman of the meeting of petitioners called to initiate the Society (p. 5), was variously described as 'First Amateur Mathematician of Scotland' and as one possessing a 'profound knowledge of mathematics'. Perhaps under the heading of mathematicians should be included Sir John Sinclair, Bt (1754–1835), who about 1792 compiled *The Statistical Account of Scotland* from data supplied by the parish ministers of that period. As Clement and Robertson point out, Sir John gave a new meaning to the word *statistical*—'the quantum of happiness enjoyed by a country's inhabitants'.

The Society has always been fortunate in having among its Fellowship men of action and among these Dr Patrick Neill (1776–1851) has an honoured place. He was a well known pteridologist, botanist and horticulturist and in addition to being Secretary of the Wernerian Society was founder of the printing firm which, for nearly 190 years, printed the Society's *Transactions*. He also founded the Neill Prize (p. 152).

An outstanding achievement in astronomy, for which he was awarded the Gunning–Victoria Prize, was made by the Rev. T. D. Anderson, a D.Sc. in classical philology, who with the aid of a pocket telescope and a small-scale star-atlas discovered a new star, *Nova Aurigae*. He communicated his discovery anonymously to the Astronomer Royal for Scotland, Dr R. Copeland, who with Dr L. Becker, read a paper on the subject to the Society (*Trans.*, 1891–93, **37**, 51).

Two Fellows from south of the Border deserve mention.

James Prescott Joule (1818–89; Hon. F.R.S.E., 1867), an amateur physicist, was one of the founders of thermodynamics (p. 47). The other was the gifted 'Leisured amateur' Fox Talbot (1800–77), a polymath—mathematician, chemist, botanist, physicist, philologist and artist—who in 1839 invented the calotype process on which modern photography is based.

An amateur archaeologist of unusual diligence and ability was J. Y. Simpson (1811–70) (p. 99), who in spite of the demands of a huge practice published many articles on various aspects of this subject (see, e.g. p. 70). The preservation of the broch at Edin's Hall was due to his spirited intervention.

It need scarcely be added that over the two hundred years of its existence an untold number of Fellows and others have given generously of their time, energy and money to the Society. At the risk of being invidious two names may be mentioned: Robert Cormack (p. 75) and Lord Fleck of Saltcoats, Chairman of Imperial Chemical Industries Ltd (p. 122).

The term amateur may perhaps be extended to men with a scientific training who take up business appointments and yet in their spare time retain an active interest in science. To this category belong Dr (later Sir) Ernest Wedderburn (1884–1958) and Andrew White Young (1891–1968), both of whom entered the legal profession, but continued Chrystal's investigations into the temperature seiches[5] of Loch Earn and other Scottish lochs, the results of which are to be found in *Transactions*, 1903–05, **41**, 823. These researches continue an old interest of the Society in the Highland lochs, Thomas Fleming, for example, nearly two hundred years ago having read a paper entitled 'Agitation on Loch Tay' (*Trans.*, 1788, **1**, 200).

'The tradition of mutual cooperation between professional and amateur, so notably evident among nineteenth century naturalists,[6] happily still survives and I have shared its benefits' (*Proc.*, 1955, **66B**, 131). This comment by a brilliant self-educated Orcadian, Robert Rendall,[7] is to be found in a paper on 'Mollusca Orcadensia' and reminds us that the amateur still has his part to play. At the present time Lord Cameron (F.R.S.E., 1949; President, 1973–76), 'an incorrigible amateur' in his own words, whose contribution to the cultural and artistic life of Edinburgh is difficult to exaggerate, shows that a busy professional life can go hand in hand with a diversity of other activities, particularly those pertaining to the Capital. In proposing the toast 'The Memory of Sir Walter Scott' on one occasion Cameron referred to the 'fame of one who so deeply loved her people and her history and the sights and the sounds of her streets'. Might these words not be applied to the thirty-first President of the Society as well as to the third?

Notes

1 In the early years of the Society the professional scientist had not yet made his appearance except in the universities.

2 The extraordinary precautions taken to conceal the authorship are described in the booklet *The Story of William and Robert Chambers* (W. and R. Chambers Ltd).

3 Charles R. Darwin (1809–82), an Honorary Fellow and polymath—botanist, zoologist, geologist and palaeontologist—was unable to participate in the Society's activities.

4 See *Brit. J. Hist. Sci.*, 1970–71, **5**, 96.

5 A *seiche* is a standing oscillation of a lake or loch, generally in the direction of the greatest length.

6 See, e.g. *The Heyday of Natural History*, 1820–70, by Lynn Barber (Jonathan Cape, 1980).

7 See Stanley Cursiter's *Looking Back* (1974).

CHAPTER V

Debate—Controversy

It is well known that scientific controversy from the lives of Leibnitz and Newton down to the present day has been often conducted with great freedom and even asperity.

Excerpt from R.S.E. Council Minutes, 26 November 1869

A learned society should act as a stimulus and catalyst to the active minds of its Fellows, and the Royal Society of Edinburgh is no exception. Freedom to debate and discuss all aspects of a problem is accepted as the right of Fellows even if occasionally this leads to dispute or controversy. It cannot, however, be sufficiently stressed that the Society refrains from 'taking sides' on the topics, scientific and literary, which are debated at its meetings or published in *Transactions* or *Proceedings*. This follows the example of the Royal Society of London, the *Philosophical Transactions* of which at one time contained a notice to the effect that '. . . it is an established rule of the Society, to which they will always adhere, never to give their opinion, as a Society, upon any subject, either of Nature or Art, that comes before them'.

The Royal Society of Edinburgh, though never acting as referee, has witnessed many thrilling contests, and in fact in the first volume of *Transactions* James Hutton (1726–97) published two papers each of which resulted in controversy. His famous 'Theory of the Earth' (p. 9), triggered off a controversy which Principal Forbes described as '. . . the Vulcanist and Neptunist war [which] raged in the hall of this Society and in the class-room of the University'. The other paper 'Theory of Rain' was strongly criticised by the French savant, M. de Luc, and was defended by Hutton in *Transactions* 'with a little asperity'.

In his major paper Hutton was the first to realise the importance of geological time, a subject which ever since has attracted the

63

attention of many scientists. Hutton saw 'no vestige of be-ginning' much to the horror of theologians who shared Bishop Ussher's belief that the date of the creation was 4004 B.C. Kelvin later calculated the age of the Earth to be 40 million years and thus started a long controversy with Archibald Geikie, who visualised an age of 100 million years. Modern ideas of time have been revolutionised by the use of new techniques and Arthur Holmes (p. 90) in the 1940s attributed ages of at least 4000 million years to many rocks (see, e.g. 'A Revised Geological Time Scale', *Trans. Edin. Geol. Soc.*, 1959, **17**, 183, also Dr S. Moorbath's lecture to the Society, 5 March 1979, entitled 'The Nature and Significance of the Oldest Terrestrial Rocks'.) Clearly Hutton's speculations have stimulated much thought since they were delivered to the Society in 1785.

The fruitfulness of debate and controversy is instanced by Sir James Hall, one of Hutton's many friends, who stated that: 'After three years of almost daily warfare with Dr Hutton on the subject of the theory, I began to view the fundamental principles with less and less repugnance'. In other words he was converted (p. 86). Some years later Sir James was on the receiving end of controversy when after a visit to France he addressed the Society on Lavoisier's 'New Theory of Chemistry' (p. 22).

Hutton's achievements continue to give rise to discussion and it has been pointed out that his *Theory of the Earth* was anticipated by Robert Hooke, whose system of the Earth published post-humously as *Discourse of Earthquakes* (1705) is almost identical to that of Hutton (Ellen T. Drake, *Amer. J. Sci.*, 1981, **281**, 963). Hooke may have been unfortunate in announcing his theory before people's minds were ready to receive it, for as Max von Laue stated: 'a discovery should only be dated from the time when it was expressed so clearly and distinctly as to influence further progress.' Hutton's theory on the other hand occasioned further investigation by colleagues and others such as Sir James Hall, Robert Jameson, John Playfair and Lord Webb Seymour (1777–1819). Playfair and Webb Seymour, for example, examined in-trusive granite veins in Glen Tilt (*Trans.*, 1816, **7**, 303). Hutton's *Theory*, as we shall see, triggered off a massive controversy (p. 86) and influenced future progress in a way not achieved by previous workers in the field. The Society has indeed cause to be grateful to Hutton and his colleagues not only for creating an interest in geology throughout the United Kingdom but also for establishing the reputation of the Society in the scientific world.

A Fellow who stoutly defended the Wernerian viewpoint (p. 86) in the Society's meetings and who was involved throughout his life in controversy of one kind or another was Thomas Thomson (1773–1852), a polymath (chemist, mathematician, mineralogist and geologist), Regius Professor of Chemistry in Glasgow (1818–52).[1] He spent eleven years (1800–11) as a private teacher of chemistry in Edinburgh and during this period wrote his very successful textbook, *A System of Chemistry* (1st edition, 1802).[2] An unfavourable review of the book in the *Edinburgh Review* (1804, **4**, 120) greatly annoyed Thomson, who answered his critic in a pamphlet and christened the journal the 'Stinkpot of Literature'. There was some substance in the *Review*'s strictures, as well as in the vicious criticism of another of his books, *An Attempt to Establish the First Principles of Chemistry* (1825), by Berzelius who wrote: 'This work belongs to those few productions from which science will derive no advantage whatsoever. Much of the experimental part, even of the fundamental experiments, appears to have been made at the writing desk; and the greatest civility which his contemporaries can show its author, is to forget it was ever published' (*Berz. Jahresbericht*, 1827, **vi**, 77).[3] These 'foul aspersions' and the slur on his integrity as a scientist were answered by Thomson, who, however, in his reply very magnanimously stated that he would 'continue to speak of [Berzelius] with that respect for his talents and industry which I feel'. The main cause of Berzelius' outburst was Thomson's support of Prout's hypothesis and its implications. It is only fair to add that years later (1829) Berzelius confessed to James F. W. Johnston (1796–1855) that 'he would willingly withdraw the offensive words in regard to Thomson's book' and allowed that Thomson was the most learned chemist in England (*Edin. J. Sci.*, 1830, N.S., **2**, 204).

Thomson's support of Dalton's theory was both perceptive and courageous, especially when one remembers that the theory was not universally accepted by chemists until well into the 19th century (p. 111). George Wilson in his inaugural address (1856) in Edinburgh stated that 'Gregory will discuss critically the arguments which can be used in defence and denial of the existence of atoms and the vindication of the atomic theory' and five years later Crum Brown in his Edinburgh M.D. Thesis stated that 'the very existence of the atoms is hypothetical'. Some scientists believed that atoms were convenient 'constructs', mental pictures which probably did not have any 'real existence', but enabled scientists to explain physical processes. Even as late as 1870 Sir B. C. Brodie was attempting to explain chemistry without the use of atoms. Atoms remained within the chemist's domain until the discovery of X-rays and radio-activity resulted in the physicist's entry into this field culminating in C. T. R. Wilson's cloud chamber investigations. Sad to say these epoch-making developments seem to have passed unnoticed at the time by the Society (p. 112).

Another Glasgow professor who moved in a world of controversy was John Anderson (1726–96) who in a most remarkable Will and Testament suggested the founding of Anderson's University, but left no money for the purpose![4] His valuable collection of scientific instruments and excellent library, however, formed a useful nucleus round which to build the new institution, successively known as Anderson's Institution (1796–1828), Anderson's University (1828–77), Anderson's College (1877–86), The Glasgow and West of Scotland Technical College (1886–1912), and The Royal Technical College, Glasgow (1912–64). It did not receive full university status until 1964 when, under the Principalship of Sir Samuel Curran (F.R.S.E., 1947), it was established by Charter as the University of Strathclyde. It is difficult to imagine a greater contrast than that between the brilliant but uncompromising John Anderson and the genial and diplomatic Sir Samuel, who tended so lovingly the flower sown some 170 years previously by his predecessor.

A unique controversy was occasioned by a paper in *Transactions* (1841, **15**, 229) in which Dr Samuel M. Brown claimed to have transmuted carbon into silicon, or more correctly to have transmuted a compound containing carbon, paracyanogen, into silicon. In this way he believed he had found evidence that 'carbon and silicon are only different forms of the same substance'. Brown was no charlatan and was regarded by his friends as an enthusiastic and careful experimenter. Other workers, however, were unable to substantiate Brown's claims. Two English chemists, Dr Brett and Mr Denham Smith, obtained by Brown's process a product which they regarded as 'carbon in a very uncombustible state'—a rather unsatisfactory statement (*Phil. Mag.*, 1841, **19**, 295). Much more thorough and equally unsuccessful were a whole series of experiments carried out by Professor George Wilson, a friend of Brown and a very respected Fellow of the Society (*Trans.*, 1844, **15**, 547). Brown to the end of his life held firmly to his belief, a belief shared by his assistants, J. Crombie Brown and A. Craig, who maintained that 'we have seen him [Samuel Brown] transmute carbon into silicon again and again'. It is therefore surprising that Crombie Brown should have been one of George Wilson's assistants in what proved to be 'four months of failure' to repeat the transmutation claimed by Samuel Brown.

Faulty interpretation of experimental results is, however, not confined to the distant past. In 1930 James Kendall undertook an investigation on the atomic weight of calcium in certain potassium bearing rocks after being assured by a colleague in America that these rocks contained significant quantities of the calcium isotope Ca^{41}. This opinion, based on magneto-optic measurements, was later shown to be erroneous. The rocks contained not a trace of the isotope.

To revert to Samuel Brown's experiments it must be remembered that in the early part of the nineteenth century there was uncertainty as to the existence and composition of the elements. David Low (1786–1859), Professor of Agriculture in Edinburgh University, for example, regarded all elements as compounds of carbon, hydrogen and oxygen (*Phil. Mag.*, 1844, **24**, 296). Nitrogen according to Low was thus an isomer of carbon monoxide. There was also much discussion on the nature of chlorine. Dr John Davy, a brother of Sir Humphry, who worked partly in London and partly in Hope's laboratory in Edinburgh, supported Sir Humphry's view that chlorine is an element, in contrast to Dr John Murray who held that it contained oxygen and was in fact oxymuriatic acid (*Trans.*, 1815–18, **8**, 287). Dr John Murray (1778–1820), an extra-mural lecturer in natural philosophy, materia medica and pharmacy, must have been a man of conviction not to say courage to dispute publicly the opinion of Sir Humphry Davy. Murray's paper was followed by one from Andrew Ure, Professor of Natural Philosphy in the Andersonian Institution, which includes the surprising statement that: 'Iodine is not entitled to rank in the same class with chlorine, but with sulphur'.

It is inevitable in a Society such as the R.S.E. with many distinguished Fellows of character and personality who are able to express themselves clearly and forcibly that occasionally severe differences of opinion result. Sir William Hamilton (1788–1856), for example, sometimes used 'language more emphatic than choice' and Tait said of him: 'There are two Sir William Hamiltons connected with the University of Edinburgh, Sir William Hamilton, Knight and Mathematician, and Sir William Hamilton, Baronet and Blockhead'. Fortunately in most instances the warmth of debate and difference of opinion is not accompanied by forfeiture of friendship and respect.[5] Tait and Kelvin were friends for some forty years, but as Kelvin wrote in his obituary notice of Tait: 'I cannot say our meetings were never ruffled. We had keen differences (much more frequently agreements). . . . We never agreed to differ, but always fought it out. But it was almost as great a pleasure to fight with Tait as to agree with him. His death is a loss to me which cannot, as long as I live, be replaced'. One can visualise these discussions between the two giants in the Royal Institution or in Tait's house in George Square. Tait and Kelvin combined forces in a controversy with John Tyndall on the relative claims of J. R. Mayer and Joule in propounding the principle of the conservation of energy.[6] In contrast to the vigour and acrimony of this controversy is the moderation with which Tait discussed the same topic with Helmholtz. A calm examination of the facts shows that although Mayer undoubtedly expressed the great principle in 1842–45, it was Joule who not only proved the truth of the law, but also—to use Joule's own words—was 'the first to give a decisive proof of this theory'. It should be stressed, however, that Mayer and Joule remained on the friendliest terms with Mayer referring to 'his dear cooperator Joule'. Joule also corresponded amicably with Tyndall (*Phil. Mag.*, 4th series, 1862, **24**, 121, 173).

Mayer was not the only one to suffer from lack of recognition. Joule on three occasions expounded his theory to the British Association, but received a chilly response. Indeed his work would have gone unheeded, but for the presence of William Thomson (later Lord Kelvin). Joule described the scene many years later:

The communication would have passed without comment if a young man had not risen in the section, and by his intelligent observations created a lively interest in the new theory. The young man was William Thomson, who had two years previously passed the University of Cambridge with the highest honours and is now probably the foremost scientific authority of the age.

Tait was one who reacted sharply to anything he considered unfair or unjust either to himself or to his colleagues. He defended himself against Clausius who accused him of misrepresentation and he supported James D. Forbes in his battle against Tyndall. Forbes carried out important investigations on the movements of glaciers and regarded a glacier as an imperfect fluid or viscous body. Tyndall pointed out that previous work on the subject had been done by Louis Rendu and accused Forbes of not giving due credit to Rendu, and Forbes, perhaps unduly sensitive to what he regarded as an attack on his integrity, reacted angrily. The two protagonists descended to personalities with deplorable results. Here again Rendu, the earlier worker, is entitled to considerable credit for his investigations, but it was the later worker, Forbes, who not only observed but also measured glacier movements and thus 'put the subject on the map' (p. 45).[7] Forbes also quarrelled with Agassiz (1807–73) on the 'veined structures' of ice in glaciers. There is no doubt that both men observed these structures, but it probably was Forbes who first recognised their importance and published his observations on them.[8]

The Society in its long history has been mercifully free from dissension (see, however, p. 26), but inevitably differences of opinion have occasionally resulted in unseemly skirmishes and quarrels. In 1799 Council decided that all Fellows must purchase the *Transactions* of the Society. Not without some reason Professor John Rotheram (1750–1804), Professor of Natural Philosophy at St Andrews, objected to this decision, but in the course of making his opinion known in a letter to Lord Dunsinnane (1731–1811) a Vice-President of the Society, he said some harsh things about the Society and its publications of which the following extract is typical: '. . . I have long observed with the greatest regret, that the Society is managed by a Junto (who, it is well known have shown their prejudice against the productions of respectable scholars in the meanest possible way, and who may be supposed to be partial to those they can make their tools) and the Papers published in the *Transactions* are for the most part highly disgraceful to the Society, and to the state of the Science in the Nation, viz., Mathematical papers with blunders even every schoolboy is capable of detecting . . .'. Even when allowance is made for the freedom with which scholars sometimes expressed themselves in the early nineteenth century this was strong language. Council took umbrage (23 November 1799) and recommended unanimously that Rotherham be expelled, a recommendation which was ratified at a General Meeting two days later. John Leslie in 1794 also referred to the 'proceedings of incorporated Juntos' after having one of his scientific papers rejected by the Society and had earlier stated his determination 'to have no connection with these incorporations called Royal Societies'. This was a somewhat ingenuous statement as he had already had a paper published by the Society (p. 107) and later accepted Fellowship.

Expulsions from the Society have been rare, although a few 'rejections' have been reported for failure of Fellows to pay subscription arrears (see, e.g. p. 72). Resignations have been more numerous, mostly for domestic reasons, but the contentious William Hamilton resigned in 1835 as the result of an argument over the diminished role of the Literary Class. Piazzi Smyth was another who resigned in pique, but after a few days was persuaded to withdraw his resignation. He did not, however, withdraw his resignation from the Royal Society in London and thereafter designated himself as 'Charles Piazzi Smyth, Late F.R.S.'.

A controversy was initiated in 1868 by Piazzi Smyth, who was greatly interested in the Great Pyramid of Cheops and on the basis of his measurements of the Pyramid reached certain fanciful and mystical conclusions (p. 74). James Y. Simpson[9] (p. 99) was a keen archaeologist and wrote a lengthy article in *Proceedings* (1868–69, **6**, 243) strongly criticising Piazzi Smyth's ideas and conclusions. Needless to say this was immediately followed by another paper from the irrepressible Piazzi (*ibid.*, 1868–69, **6**, 316). Time has dealt unkindly with Piazzi Smyth's ideas, but one thing is certain: both protagonists greatly enjoyed the controversy. What is perhaps most remarkable was the ability of Simpson amid the 'incessant distraction of practice' to find time and energy to write a polemical paper in which every statement had to be weighed and considered. To test Piazzi's calculations and write his own paper he devoted three weeks to intensive study of decimals and the perusal of journals. Yet this was the man who averred that he had 'no sufficient industry and endurance for the pursuit of any tedious and protracted investigation'. Simpson, it may be added, was frequently praised for the accuracy and sheer professionalism of his archaeological researches, though at times he could be very dogmatic in his conclusions.

A macabre note was introduced into the proceedings of the Society through no wish of the Fellows by repercussions of the Burke and Hare murders, when Robert Knox, the anatomist and a Fellow, was the subject of great controversy and suspicion. In his *Journal* Scott states that on 14 January 1829 he 'called on Mr Robison (General Secretary of the Society) and instructed him to call a meeting of the Council of the Royal Society of Edinburgh, as Mr Knox proposes to read an essay on some dissections. A bold proposal truly coming from one who has so lately the boldness of trading so deeply in human flesh. I will oppose his reading in the present circumstances if I should stand alone, but I hope he will be wrought to withdraw his essay or postpone it at least. It is very bad taste to push forward just now'. According to Scott, Knox refused to withdraw his paper, but agreed to postpone reading it to the Society.[10] Some years later Knox was again involved in controversy (p. 72).

The Society was further involved in the Burke and Hare affair, although indirectly, when a Committee of Enquiry was instituted to assess Knox's guilt or innocence. It is a measure of the Society's standing that of the nine members of the Committee seven were Fellows: Sir John Robison (Chairman), James Russell (1754–1836) (Professor of Clinical Surgery), J. Shaw Stewart (Advocate), W. P. Alison (Professor of the Theory of Physic), William Hamilton (Professor of Universal History), George Ballingall (1780–1855) (Professor of Military History) and Thomas Allan (Banker). The Committee acquitted Knox of having any knowledge that murder had been used to provide 'subjects' for his dissecting room and Cockburn in his 'Memorials' states categorically '. . . our anatomists were spotlessly correct and Knox the most correct of them all'. The findings of the Committee pleased Knox but not the citizens of Edinburgh, and Knox became embittered and convinced that he was the victim of persecution. His relationship with the Fellows disintegrated until some years later he held them in contempt. To a colleague he said: 'Why should you throw away your money upon a Society rapidly hastening to the guidance of banker's clerks, fifth-rate medical practitioners and the like. You gain nothing of Science, and as little honour.' None the less Knox continued his Fellowship until 1847 when he was 'ejected' for failing to pay his subscription. A year later his name was removed from the Roll ('election cancelled'), a vindictive decision unworthy of a learned society.

Notes

1   J. B. Morrell. *Brit. J. Hist. Sci.*, 1969, **4**, 245.
2   Dalton encouraged Thomson to publish in the third edition of his *System of Chemistry* (1807) a summary of the atomic theory.
3   Thomson carried out a great number of atomic weight determinations, but his experimental methods were open to criticism and many of his results may have been obtained by half-trained students. Berzelius had, therefore, some justification for criticism. See W. V. Farrar, *Brit. J. Hist. Sci.*, 1964–65, **2**, 297–323.
4   Anderson bequeathed his property 'to the public for the good of all mankind and the improvement of science, in an institution to be denominated Anderson's University'. It says much for the 81 Trustees whom he appointed that without any money from the bequest the College was founded. Anderson's liberal and advanced views are evidenced by his insistence that his institution was 'to admit the fair sex to the temple of knowledge on the same footing with men'.
5   'Iron sharpeneth iron: so a man sharpeneth the countenance of his friend. And friends here learn to sharpen each other's wits without ceasing to be friends.' These words, based on the Book of Proverbs, were addressed by Crum Brown to the Royal Medical Society of Edinburgh in 1896 and can be applied without fear of contradiction to our Society today.
6   For a discussion of the Joule-Mayer controversy see J. T. Lloyd, *Notes Rec. Roy. Soc. Lond.*, 1970, **25**, 211.
7   See The Theory of Glaciers, J. S. Rowlinson. *Notes Rec. Roy. Soc. Lond.*, 1971, **26**, 189.
8   It is difficult to disagree with the conclusion of I. Campbell and D. Hutchison in their critical account of the Forbes–Agassiz controversy that: 'The researcher is left regretting only that little misunderstandings could raise to this pitch, a relatively small squabble and make impossible a potentially valuable scientific cooperation' (*Isis*, 1978, **69**, 388).
9   Simpson is, of course, remembered for his discovery of chloroform as an anaesthetic.
10 There is something of a mystery about Scott's concern. His statement in his *Journal* (14 January 1829) that Mr Knox 'proposes to read an essay on some dissections' is strange in view of the fact that the billet (16 January 1829) calling the meeting (19 January) contains no mention of such a paper.

CHAPTER VI

Angular Fragments

What we call sciences are but angular fragments struck from the sphere of Omniscience, to which fresh chips from time to time are added.

From the Inaugural Address to the University of Edinburgh on 7 November 1855 by Professor George Wilson (1818–59).

In this chapter brief accounts are given of those sciences which have occupied the attention of the Society over a long period of years. No claim of completeness is made and the choice of topics is necessarily arbitrary. In spite of its brevity, however, it is hoped that the chapter will be sufficiently comprehensive to depict the part played by the Society and its Fellows in the development of the major sciences such as mathematics and natural philosophy as well as others of less general scope such as meteorology or oceanography which have been of particular interest to Fellows. For more exhaustive treatment of some of the sciences readers are referred to a series of articles under the heading 'The Biological Sciences' edited by Professor W. W. Fletcher (F.R.S.E., 1967) to be published in *Proceedings B* and to a book in preparation on the history of Scottish Astronomy by Professor Emeritus Hermann Brück.

This chapter also includes a section on the transactions of the Literary Class.

Astronomy

One of the earliest Fellows was Robert Blair (1752–1828), the first Regius Professor of Practical Astronomy at Edinburgh University. The post was a sinecure and the appointment was surprising: to appoint the First Commissioner of the Board for the Care of Sick and Wounded Seamen to a Chair is to say the least unusual.[1] Yet in both positions Blair made useful contributions. He discovered a method for preserving lime juice, a discovery of great benefit to seamen on long voyages, and later he made substantial improvements in optical lenses and telescopes. His one contribution to the Society seems to have been his paper 'On the Unequal Refrangibility of Light' (*Trans.*, 1791, **3**, 3).

The first half of the nineteenth century saw little interest in astronomy among the Fellows and only a few papers on the subject by John Robison, John Playfair and others are to be found in *Transactions*. Things changed, however, with the advent of Charles Piazzi Smyth (1819–1900), who became Astronomer Royal for Scotland (1846–88). He was named Piazzi after the well-known Italian astronomer of that name and 'he was one of the most colourful personalities of the nineteenth century'. He made notable contributions to solar spectroscopy and optics and he was the first to use a magnesium flash in photography when he took a photograph inside the Great Pyramid. He was also responsible for making the arrangements for the one o'clock gun to fire from Edinburgh Castle and the functioning of the time signal on the Nelson Monument on Calton Hill. The system still works efficiently. Piazzi Smyth was impetuous and eccentric (p. 70) and his reputation suffered considerably from his work on the Great Pyramid, although his earlier researches in which he measured the size and dimensions of the passages and inner chambers were sufficient to gain for him the Keith Prize (1865–67) (p. 70). Previous workers had sought to link the angles and dimensions of the passages in the Pyramids with astronomical significance (see, e.g. Sir John F. W. Herschel's 'Observations on the Entrance Passages of the Pyramids of Gizeh', *Phil. Mag.*, 1844, **24**, 481), but Piazzi allowed his scientific work to be submerged by fruitless, mystical speculations. He came to the conclusion that 'The Great Pyramid is not altogether of human origination' and attempted to relate the 'sacred cubit' used in building the Great Pyramid to that used by Noah in making the Ark and by Moses in making the Tabernacle (p. 70). It is only right to remember that other scientists have had mystic leanings and Napier, for example, studied for years the Revelation of St John and came to some unacceptable conclusions. Piazzi Smyth's fanciful speculations must not be allowed to obscure his great achievements and as Dr M. J. Smyth (F.R.S.E., 1965) pointed out to the Society in April 1969 'present day investigations in infrared astronomy are a continuation of the brilliant work begun more than a hundred years earlier by Piazzi Smyth'. Piazzi Smyth's excellent diagrammatic coloured representation of spectra is well exemplified by his paper in *Transactions*, 1884, **32**, 415.

Towards the end of the last century evidence was accumulated to indicate the existence of a ninth planet of the solar system and George Forbes (1849–1936) was engaged on the problem for some 30 years (*Proc.*, 1880, **10**, 426, 428, 636; 1902, **23**, 370).

Astronomers Royal for Scotland have followed Piazzi Smyth's example and have made notable contributions to the Society's activities. Ralph Allen Sampson carried out investigations on a wide range of topics including the theory and practice of accurate time-keeping and particularly the use of free pendulum clocks for precision time-keeping. His pioneer work on stellar spectra was continued by his successor, William M. H. Greaves (1897–1955), who with Dr Edwin Baker (1891–1980) carried out a great volume of precise spectral measurements. Greaves was also greatly interested in correlating temporary phenomena of the sun with terrestrial effects, a subject which had occupied the attention of John Allan Broun[2] many years previously (p. 42).

Professors Hermann Brück (F.R.S.E., 1958) and Vincent C. Reddish (F.R.S.E., 1965) have taken a leading part in the administration of the Robert Cormack Bequest and its activities. Mr Robert Cormack was a business man who rose from the position in Jenners of cash-boy to that of managing director and left a bequest of about £56,000 to the Society, to be used to promote Astronomical Knowledge and Research in Scotland. Details on how best to implement this instruction were drawn up by Professor R. A. Sampson and as a result the Bequest programme has consisted of addresses to the Society on astronomical topics, awards of Research Fellowships, visits of school parties to observatories and lectures to schools all over Scotland. The 16 visits to observatories and 111 lectures to schools in 1968–69 exemplify the popularity of these ventures, a popularity which has led to such a great demand for admission tickets that applications have frequently had to be refused. Public lectures are occasionally organised such as those given by Professor Sir Bernard Lovell, Director of the Nuffield Radio Astronomy

Laboratory, on 'Our Present Knowledge of the Universe' and by Professor Emeritus Bart J. Bok, University of Arizona, on 'Our Big and Beautiful Milky Way'.

Botany

For a long period botany was the basis of medicine and all the great botanists of early days were medical men. In line with this the botany chair in Edinburgh University was termed the Chair of Medicine and Botany and it was not until 1879 that Medicine was omitted. The independence of medicine and botany within the University was finally effected in 1969 when the Chair of Botany was removed from the Medical Faculty to the Science Faculty.

It is greatly to the credit of the early botanists that they did not confine their attention to plants of medicinal value only, but included the entire plant kingdom in their observations and thus laid the foundations upon which modern botany rests. It is understandable that the teaching of botany combined with that of medicine and materia medica left little time for original research, but John Hope (1725–86) established himself in the University of Edinburgh as an outstanding botanist. He is commemorated in *Hopea*, a genus of trees from south-east Asia. Other botanists were Daniel Rutherford (1749–1819) and Robert Graham (1786–1845), the latter having to his credit the notable feat of establishing a botanic garden in Glasgow and moving one in Edinburgh.

It is not surprising that medical practitioners would encourage the laying out of Physick Gardens so that they could obtain the necessary medicinal plants and at the same time give the medical students first-hand experience of their stock in trade, their *materia medica*. Edinburgh was no exception and its Royal Botanic Garden is the offspring of the earlier physick gardens (see, e.g. *The Royal Botanic Garden, Edinburgh, 1670–1970* by Harold R. Fletcher and William H. Brown). Until 1956 the duties and responsibilities of the Professor of Botany were held jointly with those of the Regius Keepership of the Garden.

A Scottish botanist and Honorary Fellow who spent most of his life out of Scotland was Robert Brown (1773–1858), the son of a Montrose clergyman. He travelled widely and established himself as Humboldt's *facile princeps botanicorum*. He is perhaps best known for his discovery of Brownian movement (1827), but in a very important paper on the Orchids and Asclepiads he described for the first time the cell nucleus and is thus the forerunner of John Goodsir and R. L. C. Virchov (1821–1902; Hon. F.R.S.E., 1868). One of the people to whom he demonstrated the nucleus was the young Darwin. Among other of his discoveries were the streaming movements in the hairs of *Tradescantia*.

Brown became the first Keeper of Botany in the Museum of Natural History at Kensington and for obvious reasons was unable to take part in the Society's activities, and botanical contributions to the Society rest mainly on three Edinburgh University Professors of Botany: John Hutton Balfour, his son Isaac Bayley Balfour, and W. Wright Smith. John Hutton Balfour (1808–84) is remembered for his facile pen and articles in encyclopaedias, magazines and the Society's *Transactions*, and as a great teacher who introduced laboratory work into the botany curriculum. He led many botanical excursions, one of which with friends in 1847 became famous and the resultant 'Battle of Glen Tilt' was the subject of both prose and verse. On this occasion Balfour and his party were accused of trespassing and a skirmish between the botanists and the Duke of Atholl and his retainers resulted. Some sixty years earlier James Hutton at the invitation of a previous Duke had explored the Glen.[3]

Balfour was followed by Alexander Dickson (1836–87), who, freed from having to teach medicine as well as botany (p. 76), made the most of his opportunities by carrying out research in flower-morphology and teratology and his illustrations of plants added to the attractiveness of his papers in *Transactions*. His tenure in the Chair was short as he died in 1887.

The second half of the nineteenth century witnessed a renaissance in botanical research in the United Kingdom. Previous to this emphasis had been laid on a study of the dead plant and the stimulating ideas of the life history of plants, which prevailed on the Continent, were largely ignored. The languishing science of botany was revived by a number of young botanists including T. H. Huxley, F. O. Bower (1855–1948), and last but not least Isaac Bayley Balfour (1853–1922), who succeeded Dickson in the Edinburgh Chair. He travelled widely and collected many plants and in a long, beautifully illustrated paper occupying a complete volume of *Transactions* (1880, **31**) gave an account of the plant life found in the Island of Socotra, situated off the north-east coast of Africa. Bayley Balfour acknowledged the assistance of other botanists, particularly Dr Schweinfurth who was exploring the island at that period and who 'with rare self-abnegation and generosity' enriched the volume by sending his whole collection and all his data to Bayley Balfour. According to Bower 'no-one ever knew Scotland botanically as well as Balfour did'.

One of Balfour's most important appointments was that of William Wright Smith (1875–1956) to be a lecturer in the University Botany Department. Wright Smith had wide experience at home and abroad and later as Professor of Botany and Keeper of the Royal Botanic Garden added greatly to the stature of the Department and the Garden. He made many contributions to botany and horticulture and his researches with Harold Fletcher were the subject of many papers including some in *Transactions*. In 1944 he became the second botanist to be elected President of the Society. Wright Smith was succeeded as Regius Keeper of the Garden by Harold Fletcher (1907–78), a Neill Prizeman and enthusiastic Fellow, generous in every way. The lay-out of the Edinburgh Royal Botanic Garden is largely of his devising and the modern glass-houses and herbarium are monuments to his genius as a fund-raiser. The present Regius Keeper is Douglas M. Henderson, who is also Curator of the R.S.E. Library and Museum.

Chemistry

Many chemists with international reputations have been Fellows of the Society, and one of the greatest is undoubtedly Joseph Black (1728–99), a Founder Member. His famous paper, 'Experiments upon Magnesia Alba, Quicklime and some other Alkaline Substances' was published first as an M.D. Thesis (1754),[4] read to the Philosophical Society in 1755, and included in that Society's *Essays and Observations, Physical and Literary* in 1756. This was 27 years before the institution of our Society and Black contributed only one paper to *Transactions*, but his name and reputation must have helped considerably to place the Society on a sound footing. Black's successor in the Edinburgh Chair of Chemistry was Thomas Charles Hope (1766–1844), who in 1798 published a paper in which he demonstrated that strontia differs from baryta and thus discovered the element Strontium (*Trans.*, 1793–97, **4**,

3). Hope also established that at low temperatures water contracts when heated and attains its maximum density at 4°C (*ibid.*, 1799–1803, **5**, 379).

Another addition to the list of chemical elements (cf. p. 67) was made by Daniel Rutherford. Andrew Lang in his book *Walter Scott* makes a curious and somewhat ambiguous remark about him: 'Scott's maternal uncle, Dr Rutherford, "one of the best chemists in Europe"—we have Sir Walter's word for it'. In a thesis submitted in 1772 to the University of Edinburgh for the M.D. degree entitled 'De aere fixo dicto, aut mephitico', he recognised nitrogen as a separate constituent of the atmosphere, a constituent which is non-inflammable and does not support combustion. Rutherford was unaware that Priestley some months earlier had made the same discovery.[5]

The later years of the eighteenth century and the early years of the nineteenth mark a seminal period in the history of chemistry and give rise to the description made by James Hall in 1805 of 'the very imperfect state of chemistry which has only of late years begun to deserve the name of a science'. That period lies between the death of phlogiston and the birth of the atomic theory: between Lavoisier's *Traité Elementaire de Chemie* (1789) and Dalton's *New System of Chemical Philosophy* (1808). Lavoisier's book was translated into English and published in Edinburgh under the title *Elements of Chemistry* (5 editions, 1790, 1793, 1796, 1799 and 1802) and his theory was discussed at length in the Society's rooms (p. 22).

A famous paper, entitled 'On the Law of the Diffusion of Gases' (*Trans.*, 1830–33, **12**, 222) was read by Thomas Graham (1805–69), the first President of the Chemical Society (1841–43, re-elected 1845–47), who spent half his life in Scotland and the second half in London, first as Professor of Chemistry at University College and later as Master of the Mint. He was elected to the Fellowship in 1828, age 22, one of the youngest men ever to be elected (pp. 45, 94) and was a regular attender at the Society's meetings in his younger days.

One of the successors of Graham in the Chair of Chemistry at Anderson's College was William Dittmar (1833–92) an excellent teacher and analyst who determined the atomic weight of platinum (*Trans.*, 1885–87, **33**, 561). He made important improvements in the construction and performance of the chemical balance and it was on a balance made on his instructions that many years later Mowbray Ritchie (1905–66) accurately determined the atomic weight of phosphorus, an achievement demanding exceptional skill and technique.

James Dewar's achievements in physics tend to make us forget that he was also a chemist of repute and in a notable paper read to the Society on 6 June 1870 he pointed out the similarity between the properties of derivatives of benzene and those of pyridine and advanced the formula for pyridine which gained general acceptance (*Trans.*, 1872, **26**, 189). The same formula, unknown to Dewar, had been suggested in 1869 by W. Körner, who published his idea in a little known journal. Happily as Leonard Dobbin puts it: 'No petty question of priority arose to disturb the intimate friendly relations of Körner and Dewar' and the formula is perhaps best described as the Dewar–Körner formula for pyridine. Dewar also pointed out that several structural formulae for benzene can be constructed (*Proc.*, 1869, **6**, 82). These were regarded purely as chemical curiosities until 1963 when the isomeric 'Dewar benzene' was isolated.

Crum Brown, was appointed to the Chair of Chemistry at Edinburgh in 1869. He was described as a 'master, versed in the latest results' and he had the conviction and courage to expound the significance of Mendelejeff's periodic table[6] of the chemical elements at a time when many leading chemists were still applauding the prudence of the Chemical Society which refused to publish Newlands' earlier discovery of the same fundamental law.[7] Crum Brown with Thomas Fraser carried out pioneer work on the correlation of molecular structure with pharmacological effect (*Trans.*, 1867–69, **25**, 151, 693). For this conjoint research both authors were awarded the Makdougall Brisbane Prize. With James (later Sir James) Walker he effected an elegant and novel electrosynthesis of organic acids (*Trans.*, 1889–91, **36**, 211; 1891–95, **37**, 361). His paper on the properties and formulae of organic substances led to the system of graphic representation which with minor modifications is used today (*Trans.*, 1864, **23**, 707), and is based on his 1861 Doctor of Medicine Thesis, a remarkable contribution by a young man of 23. The significance of the Thesis quite escaped the notice of the examiners.

Walker (1863–1935) succeeded Crum Brown in 1908 to the Chair of Chemistry and like Crum Brown (1891–93) became

President of the Chemical Society (1921–23). He was largely responsible for introducing against considerable opposition the new theories of solution from the Continent which were associated with the great chemists van't Hoff, Arrhenius, Ostwald and Nernst. His ability to lecture authoritatively an organic, inorganic and physical chemical topics was remarkable. While Walker was still in office George Barger (1878–1939) was appointed to the new Chair of Chemistry in relation to Medicine. Barger was in close touch with all the important continental chemical laboratories and maintained 'the old tradition of the international scholar, who was at home everywhere, where teaching was held in esteem'. His cosmopolitan outlook was evidenced in 1923 when the International Congress of Physiology was held in Edinburgh—the first important scientific congress to be held in Great Britain after the First World War. Sharpey Schafer was President and Barger Secretary of the Conference and it was largely through their efforts that the Congress was truly international with German and Austrian scientists invited.

A pioneer in the identification of pigments in paintings was Arthur Pillans Laurie (1861–1949), Principal of the Heriot-Watt College (now University).[8] Laurie's work, described in his book and in a lecture to the Society in 1911, was an important contribution to a subject which has been since revolutionised by the aid of modern sophisticated spectroscopic and microchemical methods.

From the early years of last century Fellows have engaged in the chemical investigation of complex organic substances including the alkaloids (T. Anderson, R. Christison), petroleum (Christison) and the red resin from the Dragon's Blood tree (J. J. Dobbie, 1883–1924, and G. G. Henderson). The last thirty years have witnessed a resurgence of this interest in the field by Fellows using the battery of techniques now available. Particularly worthy of mention are Lord Todd of Trumpington, (nucleic acids); Sir Harry Melville (F.R.S.E., 1937, polymers); John Monteath Robertson (F.R.S.E., 1943, X-ray crystallography); John Masson Gulland (1898–1947, alkaloids); Sir James Colquhoun Irvine (1877–1952) and Sir Edmund Hirst (1898–1975, carbohydrates). Geographical reasons prevented some of these workers from participating in the Society's activities, but an exception was Sir Edmund Hirst, whose services to science and the Society were recognised by his election to the Presidency and the award of the Gunning Victoria Jubilee Prize (1960–64) and the Bruce Preller Lectureship (1951). He was President of the Chemical Society (1956–58).

The close relationship between chemistry and biochemistry was demonstrated by J. N. Davidson when he showed by chemical means that RNA is an abundant constituent of animal cells (*Proc.*, 1944, **62B**, 96), a conclusion which was accepted with some scepticism at a time when nucleic acids excited little interest. Earlier workers in the field included Sharpey-Schafer who recognised the existence of a substance which controlled sugar metabolism and named it insuline: George Barger who with C. R. Harington (1897–1972; Hon. F.R.S.E., 1951) synthesised thyroxine: and Guy Marrian (1904–81) who isolated the steroids oestriol and pregnanediol. Lord Todd (Hon. F.R.S.E., 1966) for his work on nucleic acids and R. L. M. Synge (F.R.S.E., 1963) for his indispensable method of paper chromatography are Nobel Prizemen.

Engineering

Engineering has never been one of the Society's main interests although the Fellowship has included men such as James Watt, Lord Kelvin and Sir Alfred Ewing. James Watt, a Founder Member, did not contribute to the Society's activities and the first engineer to do so was Robert Stevenson (p. 83), who attended classes under the ebullient Professor John Anderson at Glasgow University. Anderson, as already noted (p. 66), was the founder of the Andersonian University (later Strathclyde University) from which have come many prominent Fellows including Thomas Graham, David Livingstone, Lyon Playfair and James Young. The first engineer to contribute to the Society's publications was John Scott Russell (1808–82),[9] a civil engineer who published an important paper on the resistance of water to a moving object (*Trans.*, 1837, **14**, 47). He discovered what is known as the wave of transition which accompanies a vessel and developed the 'wave-line' system of ship construction. He pioneered a scientific approach to ship-building and in collaboration with Brunel built the *Great Eastern*, the largest ship of its time and for many years afterwards. This is one of the great engineering feats of the nineteenth century and takes its place with the building of the Bell and Skerryvore lighthouses by Robert and Alan Stevenson and of the laying of the trans-Atlantic cable by Kelvin (p. 121).

Kelvin in his deep-sea cable adventures was assisted by H. C. Fleeming Jenkin (1833–85), the first Professor of Engineering in Edinburgh University (1868–85) and both, by taking out patents and acting as consulting engineers, are reported to have been well rewarded financially.

No history of the Society would be complete without reference to the Stevenson family, seven members of whom were Fellows over an unbroken period of 156 years (1815–1971). For a short period Robert and his three sons were Fellows at the same time. The family has a unique record of lighthouse building and technique, illumination and fog-signals (see *infra*) and none of them took out patents for their inventions so that their designs and improvements were freely available to all.[10] Five members served as Engineer to the Northern Lighthouse Board for a continuous period of 140 years (see Table).

Stevenson Family

(Years of service as Engineers to the N.L.B. in parentheses)

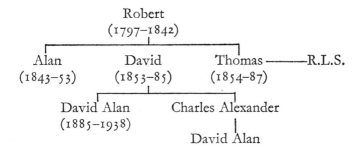

Robert Stevenson (1772–1850) is remembered mainly as the designer and builder of the Bell Rock Lighthouse (begun in 1807 and completed in 1811), a model of which, made under his supervision, may be seen in the Royal Scottish Museum in Edinburgh. The significance of this amazing and heroic feat may be realised by recalling the fearful loss of shipping round the coast of Britain at the beginning of the nineteenth century. In the storm of 1799, for example, no fewer than 70 vessels were stranded or lost on the Scottish coast alone, and in the previous year Robert Stevenson found the remains of five ships on the island of Sanday, scarcely 12 miles long. More than 150 years later another Fellow, Stanley Cursiter, recorded spending long holidays on Sanday in a 'house full of the relics of wrecked ships'. Robert Stevenson was a man of great ability and wide interests and became so well known that many letters to him were simply addressed 'Robert Stevenson, Esq., Civil Engineer, Edinburgh'. It may be noted that he never gained a university degree or passed an examination in an engineering subject. He is credited with the invention of flashing and intermittent lights for lighthouses and in another sphere of activity he designed London Road and Regent Road in Edinburgh. He discovered that salt-water of the sea flows up a river in a stream quite different from the down-flowing fresh-water. A similar investigation was carried out earlier by John Fleming (*Trans.*, 1816, **8**, 507).

Three of Robert's sons followed him as Engineers to the Northern Lighthouse Board and effected great improvements in lighthouse construction and illumination. Alan (1807–65) built several lighthouses including the famous Skerryvore lighthouse (1844), a mammoth and heroic task, while David (1815–86) introduced in 1870 the use of paraffin in lighthouses thereby greatly increasing the intensity of the light emitted.[11] Thomas (1818–87) developed the azimurthal condensing system of lighthouse illumination. He was President of the Society (1884–85). His son, Robert Louis Stevenson (p. 47) contributed a paper to the Society and his book *A Family of Engineers* is principally about his grandfather, Robert Stevenson, and the building of the Bell Rock Lighthouse.

David's son, David Alan Stevenson (1854–1938), the last of the Stevenson N.L.B. Engineers, was a cousin of R.L.S. who inscribed his short story *The Pavilion on the Links* to him. He made many improvements in coastal lighting and fog-signals and designed 22 lighthouses.

Although not Engineers to the N.L.B. two other members of the Stevenson family played a role in lighthouse history. Charles Alexander (1855–1950) invented the 'Leader Cable', a device for guiding ships into port in fog or at night (*Proc.*, 1893, **20**, 25).

Some thirty years later it came as a surprise when in 1921 the French Academy of Sciences awarded a medal for the invention not to Stevenson but to a Frenchman and this called forth from the Society a protest 'as a simple act of justice' to Charles. He also described an invention by which the transmission and reception of speech over a distance of two miles can be effected without the use of wires (*Proc.*, 1894, **20**, 196). Was this the first radio broadcast of sound? Stevenson's efforts to introduce his invention into the lighthouse field failed and Marconi a few years later was sending his first message across the Atlantic.

With the help of his son David Alan (1891–1971) Charles in 1928 installed the Clyde 'Talking Beacon' in the Cumbrae and Cloch lighthouses. The invention which enabled ships to plot their passage in fog by means of synchronised radio and fog signals was adopted by many countries but not by Great Britain. David Alan was the author of *The World's Lighthouses before 1820*, a book which placed him as the foremost authority in the field. During the last years of his life he was engaged in writing the story of the Stevenson family, but died before completing it.[12] His death brought to a close the long continuous relationship between the Society and a very remarkable family.

Geology

As noted earlier (p. 9) a lengthy paper in the first volume of *Transactions* (1788, **1**, 209) entitled 'The Theory of the Earth' earned the author, James Hutton, the title of the Founder of Modern Geology.[13] The Society was thus fortunate in having as a Founding Fellow a man, whose name in the words of Archibald Geikie (written a hundred years later) 'would become a household word in after generations and that pilgrims would come from distant lands to visit the scenes from which he drew his inspiration'. This eulogy was underlined by Serge Tomkeieff (*Proc.*, 1950, **63B**, 387): 'Such a man was Isaac Newton and such also was James Hutton. It is of little profit to argue as to which was the greater mind. What Newton achieved in the field of astronomy and mathematics Hutton achieved in the field of geology. It was he who provided geology with a theory'.

In 1795 Hutton published the *Theory* in book form in reply to a violent attack by Richard Kirwan, afterwards President of the

Royal Irish Academy. By the time the book was written Hutton was a sick man and the book in contrast to the paper is not very readable. In fact according to Roebuck: 'Hutton's writings produce a degree of obscurity astonishing to those who knew him and heard him everyday converse with no less clearness and precision, animation and force'.[14] It was left to one of Hutton's disciples, John Playfair (p. 42) to present the *Theory* in a more acceptable form entitled *Illustrations of the Huttonian Theory of the Earth* (1802), which according to Archibald Geikie 'for luminous treatment and graceful diction stands still without a rival in English geological literature'.[15] This led to a belated posthumous recognition of the *Theory*. A recent discovery of a remarkable series of drawings by Hutton's friends John Clerk of Eldin (1728–1812), John Clerk Jr (Lord Eldin, 1757–1832), and Sir James Hall gives further insight into Hutton's observations (p. ooo). In a note by the authors Professor G. Y. Craig has pointed out that the Society missed an opportunity in 1840 of publishing the drawings (see *Trans.*, 1840, **14**, footnote on p. 295).

Hutton never lacked friends and one of them, Sir James Hall (p. 43), the Father of Experimental Geology, was another who strongly supported the *Theory*. He suggested to Hutton that evidence for his *Theory* might be provided by experimentally testing the effect of heat and pressure on rocks and minerals. Hutton saw little profit from such experiments and so great was Hall's regard for the Master ('false delicacy' Brewster called it!)[16] that he did not publish his results until after Hutton's death. One of Hall's findings was based on an observation in a Leith glass works when by accident the melt consolidated with strong crystallisation. This led Hall to carry out a series of experiments which showed that in such operations the rate of cooling is critical. He demonstrated that lavas and whinstones when melted and rapidly cooled give 'identical glasses' which when remelted and slowly cooled gave 'identical crystallites' (*Trans.*, 1799–1803, **5**, 43). He followed this by fusing limestone and crystallising it to something very similar to marble under high pressure, and, more important still from a geological standpoint of view, he established that calcium carbonate when heated under high pressure does not dissociate (*Trans.*, 1804–11, **6**, 71).

Opposed to Hutton's teaching was Abraham Gottlieb Werner (1749–1817; Hon. F.R.S.E., 1807) of Freiberg in Saxony, who by persuasive exposition of his theories gained a great reputation and whom Cuvier termed the 'Great Oracle of the Sciences of the Earth'.[17] Werner found a staunch supporter in Robert Jameson (1774–1854), who as a young man in 1796 had the timerity to criticise Hutton's *Theory* in two papers he read before the Royal Medical Society of Edinburgh, to which in these days many non-medical papers were presented. Jameson remained for much of his life a Wernerian and although he is said never to have participated in the violent and acrimonious disputes indulged in by the Huttonians and Wernerians in Edinburgh (p. 23) he did not hesitate to restrict the display of specimens in the Natural History Museum to students who favoured Wernerian views. It is a measure of his stature, however, that he later publicly renounced the creed he had taught for many years and paid an uncompromising tribute to the truth and profoundity of the Huttonian *Theory*. Jameson occupied the Chair of Natural History in the University of Edinburgh for 50 years (1804–54) and his reputation rests partly on the number of his students who later distinguished themselves.[18] He played a major role in the inauguration of the Royal Scottish Museum and for his services to the City of Edinburgh he was given a civic funeral, an honour earlier accorded to James Gregory (1753–1821), Andrew Duncan *senior*, Thomas Chalmers and later to W. P. Alison and J. Y. Simpson.

After the deaths of Hutton, Playfair and Hall interest in geology at the Society's meetings waned. The Parallel Roads of Glen Roy did, however, attract attention. These roads at one time were thought to be hunting roads, but in 1805 a distinguished amateur English geologist, George Bellas Greenough,[19] made a geological tour of Scotland and concluded that 'the roads were shore beaches of a lake which had stood at three successive lower levels'. This view was later supported by Thomas Dick Lauder (1784–1848) (*Trans.*, 1818, **9**, 1) and David Milne Home (*ibid.*, 1844–49, **16**, 395; 1872–76, **27**, 595; 1876–78, **28**, 93). Agassiz completed the picture by postulating an ice barrier damming the fresh-water lake and melting at widely separated periods.[20] This idea is contained in a letter from Agassiz to Jameson which was published in *The Scotsman* (7 October 1840) (see also *Edin. New Phil. J.*, 1842, **33**, 217, 236). The glacial ice-dam theory of Agassiz encountered much opposition, but was accepted by Archibald Geikie in his *The Scenery of Scotland* (1901).

A striking feature of Dick Lauder's paper is his magnificent engravings.

A decline in matters geological in the first half of the nineteenth century both in Scotland and in the Society followed the Hutton era and indeed as late as 1862 Principal Forbes was lamenting 'the progressive decay of our once illustrious Geological School' (*Proc.*, 1864–65, **5**, 18), while three years later Christison found 'geological instruction in Edinburgh University asleep'. It is to the credit of the Society that in 1865 the President and Council petitioned the Rt Hon. Earl Russell, First Lord of the Treasury, to assist in founding a Chair of Geology in Edinburgh University, a plea supported by a letter from Christison to W. E. Gladstone, then Chancellor of the Exchequer. Both Russell and Gladstone had Edinburgh University connections, the former having studied under Playfair and the latter having served as Rector. The petition was not immediately successful, but may have served a useful purpose for when in 1871, thanks to the generosity of Sir Roderick Impey Murchison (1792–1871), a Chair of Geology was founded, the Government subsidised the Professor's income by an annual grant of £200. Sir Roderick was a geologist of repute, who as Director of the Geological Survey of Great Britain spent much of his life in London, but never forgot his native Scotland and made many tours in the Highlands. He was responsible for naming the Silurian, Devonian and Permian systems and for their first elucidation. For his contributions to geology in Scotland he was awarded the Makdougall–Brisbane Prize.

The first two occupants of the New Chair, the brothers Geikie, helped to reinstate Edinburgh as a centre of Geological research. Although they did not publish much in the Society's journals they obviously enjoyed their Fellowships as is attested by their attendance at meetings of the Society and their membership of the Royal Society of Edinburgh Club. Sir Archibald Geikie (1835–1924) as a boy while standing outside the Old College made the prophetic remark: 'Do you see that big building with the iron gates? I am going in there and one day I shall be professor there'. In the event both he and his younger brother did in fact become Professors of Geology in the University. Archibald Geikie was the first Director of the Scottish Branch of the Geological Survey (1867), first occupant of the Murchison Chair of Geology and Mineralogy in the University of Edinburgh (1871) and Director General of the Geological Survey (1882). He made great contributions to igneous geology—see, for example, his memoir on 'The History of Volcanic Action during the Tertiary Period in the British Isles' (*Trans.*, 1887–90, **35**, 21)— and his book *Ancient Volcanoes of Great Britain* was described as 'invaluable'. He secured recognition of Hutton's *Theory* (p. 9), thus supporting Playfair's earlier efforts, and enjoyed the great distinction of being awarded the Order of Merit.

James Geikie (1839–1915) succeeded his brother in the Edinburgh Chair (1882–1915). Like James D. Forbes he was greatly interested in glacial science and his book *The Great Ice Age* (1874) is a classic. In 1912 his brother, Sir Archibald, was elected President of the Royal Society of London and a year later James was elected President of the Royal Society of Edinburgh. That two brothers should at the same time hold these high offices is surely unique. Recognition of Geikie's standing in the scientific world is to be found in Mount Geikie in the Wind River of the Rocky Mountains in Wyoming. Similar recognition of Fellows is Cape Brewster, Scoresby Land and Jameson Land in East Greenland. James Geikie had a quiet but effective way of expressing himself and many will share his feelings that scientific meetings are frequently too long when he stated that '. . . the speakers not only exhausted time, but encroached upon eternity'. His recorded recreation in *Who's Who*, 'Loafing in pleasant places with a congenial friend', makes delightful reading.

Colleagues of the Geikies include Benjamin N. Peach (1842–1926) of the Geological Survey of Scotland and his collaborator John Horne (1848–1928) who covered many parts of Scotland and interpreted the geological structure of the North West Highlands. They were a delightful pair and it was said that 'to listen to their friendly discussions was both an education and an entertainment'. A simple monument at Inchnadamph is a memorial to their work. Peach was an accomplished artist and an exhibition of his water-colour paintings and pen and pencil sketches in 1980 in Murchison House attracted many visitors.

In important papers (*Trans.*, 1921, **52**, 603, 643, 831 and 855) R. Kidston (1852–1924) and William H. Lang (1874–1960) revealed the significance of an entirely new class of plants, perfectly preserved as fossils, belonging to the (then) earliest known flora of the land. These were found in the Chert of Muir of Rhynie in 1913 by the indefatigable Rev. Dr W. Mackie, a member of the Edinburgh Geological Society. Dr Kidston was a leading authority on carboniferous fossil plants and Lang a plant morphologist.

Mineralogy was a subject in which Jameson, Thomas Thomson, Thomas Allan and other Fellows were keenly interested at the beginning of last century, but undoubtedly the foremost Scottish mineralogist of the nineteenth century was M. F. Heddle (1828–98), Professor of Chemistry in the University of St Andrews. His collection of 9,000 specimens was called 'the finest national collection of the minerals of any one country in the world' and his book *The Mineralogy of Scotland* is still a standard work. The collection is now to be found in the Royal Scottish Museum. Earlier, another Professor of Chemistry at St Andrews, Arthur Connell (1794–1863), was a noted mineralogist and analyst and among his achievements he analysed and determined the structure of Greenockite (*Trans.*, 1836–40, **14**, 619). His analytic skill was demonstrated by the fact that he did so with only 0.24 g. of mineral at his disposal.

It is impossible to do justice to the many Fellows who were distinguished geologists and mention will be made of only a few. Ramsay H. Traquair (1840–1912), Keeper of the Natural History Collection in the Royal Scottish Museum (1873–1906), was a world authority on fossil fishes (see, e.g. *Trans.*, 1903, **40**, 687). He was a Neill Prizeman as was Sir John Flett (1869–1947), Director of the Geological Survey of Great Britain, who was one of five pupils who in the course of a single generation went from Kirkwall Burgh School to the University of Edinburgh and later distinguished themselves in the academic field.

It is a measure of the place geology has occupied in the Society's activities that, of the 52 Neill Prizemen, 17 have been geologists. Three are still remembered by the older generation of Fellows. Robert Campbell (1881–1957), known to generations of geology students at Edinburgh University, who served as second-in-command to three Professors—James Geikie, Thomas J. Jehu (1871–1943), and Arthur Holmes (1890–1965)—was a distinguished petrologist. Arthur Holmes, one of the great earth scientists of the century, was recognised internationally as 'the genius in the business of age-dating'. He was awarded the Makdougall Brisbane Prize for 1962–64 'in recognition of his pre-eminent contributions to the fundamental philosophy of the Earth Sciences'. Another ebullient personality was Sir Edward B. Bailey (1882–1965), Director of the Geological Survey of Great Britain, who was ever prepared to participate in the Society's discussions. Finally to complete the record comes the gentle James E. Richey (1886–1968; General Secretary, 1946–56) of the classic 'Ardnamurchan Memoir'.

Mathematics

John Napier of Merchiston is often proclaimed to be the first great scientific Scotsman and with men of the calibre of Colin Maclaurin later occupying the Chair of Mathematics at Edinburgh University it is not surprising that the Society should continue the mathematical tradition thus established. It must be admitted, however, that for more than a century the concern of the Society for mathematics never matched that held by natural philosophy.

The early *Transactions* contain contributions from mathematicians, notably John Playfair (p. 42) and John Leslie (p. 107), but the strength of these men lay in the experimental sciences such as geology. According to Cargill Knott the 'one strong mathematician of that time to whom Edinburgh can lay some claim was James Ivory (1765–1842)', the author of *Ivory's Theorem* on the law of attraction of an ellipsoid. This 'forms an important link in the chain of investigations in this difficult and fascinating study from the days of Stirling, Maclaurin and Clairaut to the refinements of Poincaré,[21] Darwin and Jeans'. Ivory was greatly interested in astronomy and enjoyed a well earned European reputation.

Leslie's successor to the Edinburgh chair was a remarkable, self-taught man, William Wallace (1768–1843), who began his working life as a bookbinder and bookseller. Later he taught mathematics at Perth Academy and while there wrote mathematical papers which Playfair considered good enough to read to the Society and publish in *Transactions*. Wallace is remembered for his invention of the copying instruments the pantograph and eidograph (*Trans.*, 1833–36, **13**, 418).

Duncan Farquharson Gregory, older brother of the Professor of Chemistry at Edinburgh University was not a Fellow, but read a paper to the Society on 'The Real Nature of Symbolical Algebra' (*Trans.*, 1836–40, **14**, 208) and with Boole is one of the founders of modern algebra.[22]

The Rev. Philip Kelland (1808–79) was the first Englishman of English education to occupy an Edinburgh Chair, but according to Grant 'came to know the Scottish Universities better even than do Scotsmen themselves'. He read many mathematical papers to the Society and he was the first to establish the Society's journals as suitable vehicles for mathematical communications. Kelland's main contributions to mathematics were on General Differentiation, the Theory of Waves and the Theory of Parallels. One of his most important papers 'On the Limits of Our Knowledge respecting the Theory of Parallels' (*Trans.*, 1862–64, **23**, 433) dealt with non-Euclidean Geometry and evoked from Tait and Chrystal (*Proc.*, 1879–80, **10**, 321) the eulogy: 'It would scarcely be possible to convey to those who have not busied themselves with pan-geometry (or the geometry of pure reason, as opposed to the geometry of experience—which is Euclid's) a full idea of the importance of this work of Kelland's, and of the evidence it affords of his grasp of purely Mathematical speculation'. Regrettably Kelland died only six months after his election as President of the Society. He was greatly loved and Robert Louis Stevenson said of him that 'when he looked at you his spectacles glittered with affection'.

Many papers on the Theory of Determinants were contributed by Sir Thomas Muir (1844–1934) and his book *Theory of Determinants in the Historical Order of Development* made him famous. According to Cargill Knott 'no mathematician's library is complete without these books of reference'. Another notable mathematician was Dr James Burgess, whose published tables of the error function (*Trans.*, 1897, **39**, 257) 'are the most complete tables ever published by the Royal Society of Edinburgh'. Edward Sang, mathematician and physicist, is mentioned elsewhere (p. 109).

At the end of last century the Fellowship included a number of mathematical school teachers. John Sturgeon Mackay (1843–1914) was a distinguished geometer who taught at Edinburgh Academy for nearly 40 years. He was the first President of the Edinburgh Mathematical Society. John Alison (1861–1952) and Anderson J. G. Barclay both taught mathematics at George

Watson's Boys' College, Edinburgh, the former becoming Headmaster.

George Chrystal (p. 48) contributed several purely mathematical papers to the Society, notably on non-Euclidean geometry. In addition he used his mathematical expertise and experimental skill to solve the problem of the Seiches of Loch Earn (*Trans.*, 1907–09, **46**, 455) (p. 61), a problem to which his attention was drawn by Sir John Murray's survey of the Scottish Fresh Water Lochs.

Chrystal was succeeded in the Edinburgh Chair by Sir Edmund Taylor Whittaker (1873–1956), formerly Royal Astronomer of Ireland and Professor of Astronomy at Trinity College, Dublin. He held the Edinburgh chair, the oldest in the Edinburgh University Arts Faculty, for 34 years and 'was one of the great mathematical scholars and teachers of the century' (*Edin. Univ. J.*, 1955–57, p. 126). Many Fellows and many generations of students remember with pleasure and admiration the clarity of his lectures. Throughout his career he published books and papers and at the age of 80 the second volume of his *History of the Theories of Aether and Electricity*, an astonishing feat. He was an extremely active Fellow and was President for five years.

One of Whittaker's postgraduate students, Alexander C. Aitken (1895–1967) followed him in the Chair. Aitken was a greatly loved and loyal Fellow and contributed frequently to the Society's proceedings. He was one of the Secretaries to the Ordinary Meetings (1936–40), a Vice-President for six years (1948–51; 1956–59), and wrote some 70 papers on statistics, numerical analysis, and algebra, many of which appeared in the *Transactions* and *Proceedings*. He had a phenomenal faculty of rapid mental calculation and an unusually developed numerical memory. 'In both respects he was at least equal to the few prodigies for whom authentic records exist' (Robert Schlapp). He was gifted in many ways and his book *Gallipoli to the Somme—Recollections of a New Zealand Infantryman* earned for him the Fellowship of the Royal Society of Literature. In his book Aitken relates that while serving with the Forces in France his attention was drawn to the loss of the platoon roll-book and he was able to provide from memory the full name and number of every man in the platoon.

By way of postscript another mathematician may be mentioned. J. H. Maclagan Wedderburn (1882–1948), brother of Sir Ernest, made first-rate contributions to modern algebra, thus following in the steps of Gregory and Boole (p. 92) and his election to the Fellowship in 1903 at the age of 21 means he was one of the youngest Fellows ever to be elected (cf. pp. 45, 79).

Medicine and the Basic Medical Sciences

It might be thought that a Society which included in its early Fellowship men such as William Cullen, Monro *secundus* (1733–1817), James Gregory, Andrew Duncan *senior* (1744–1828) and Benjamin Bell (1749–1806) would be an ideal forum for medical discussion and debate. In fact as Christison pointed out in his Presidential Address on 7 December 1868 'medicine makes only a rare, and for the most part insignificant appearance in the business of the Society'. He goes on to mention papers read to the Society including those in which Dr Hope describes a case of death from an impacted gall stone; Dr Butter reports hemlock as a sovereign cure for St Vitus's Dance; and Dr Duncan claims to have cured an inveterate hiccup with a single dose of dilute sulphuric acid. Christison comments somewhat bitingly: 'If this be all that medicine could do in its most palmy days in Edinburgh to hold up its head in the Royal Society [of Edinburgh], I confess it is not a subject of regret that, by gradual and tacit consent, papers on pure medical practice have been allowed to drop from our *Proceedings*. For assuredly there is nothing at all so remarkable or particularly instructive in death from an impacted gall-stone or from any form of hernia, as to deserve being recorded in the *Proceedings* of the Royal Society: nor would I advise patient or physician to trust much either to Dr Butter's cure for St Vitus's Dance, or to the remedy which seemed to Dr Duncan to put an end to inveterate hiccup'.

One reason for the lack of medical communications to the Society is to be found in the existence in Edinburgh of other societies where medical men could meet and discuss medical topics and which could provide publication facilities. William Gregory, for example, read his paper on the preparation of morphine hydrochloride (p. 119) to the Royal College of Physicians and published it in the *Edinburgh Medical and Surgical Journal* (1831, **35**, 331).

If purely medical matters have played only a minor role in the

Society's meetings, the same is not true of the basic sciences related to medicine. Turner made this point succinctly when he stated: 'Papers on medical questions in the more technical sense have not formed a part of the work of our Society, but the sciences on which medicine is based, and which have an application to practice, have been pursued with diligence and profit' (*Trans.*, General Index, 1889–1908, p. 1). It is therefore not surprising to find some very distinguished names in the medical Fellowship of the Society. At the beginning of the 19th century Sir Charles Bell (1774–1842) published three papers in *Transactions* which are extensions of those given to the Royal Society of London. A great surgeon and anatomist, Bell published in 1811 the results of his experiments leading to the fundamental discovery of the difference between sensory and motor nerves, experiments, which according to Turner, 'were the turning point of our present conception of the physiology of the nervous system'. Such was Bell's reputation that when he visited Roux's class in Paris Roux dismissed the class with the words: 'C'est assez, Monsieurs, vous avez vu Charles Bell'. On the accession of William IV in 1830 Bell was knighted along with three other Fellows—Ivory, Leslie and Brewster.

One of the best known Edinburgh anatomists was Robert Knox (1791–1862), a brilliant lecturer, who contributed papers to the Society even after the unfortunate Burke and Hare episode (p. 71). One of these, 'Observations on the Comparative Anatomy of the Eye' (*Trans.*, 1823–26, **10**, 43) is a notable piece of research when one considers the limitations of the microscopes then available. Other papers to the Society reflect his keen interest in his favourite hobby, fishing. Another anatomist was John Goodsir (1814–67), who stressed that the cell is the starting-point of all structures in plants and animals (*Trans.*, 1844, **15**, 295). His name is associated with that of Virchov as a pioneer in cell theory, and Virchov dedicated his *Cellular Pathologie* (1858) to him with the words 'one of the most acute observers of cell-life'.

James Syme (1799–1870) attended many of the Society's meetings, but took little part in its affairs, although he did publish an important paper in which he demonstrated the power of the Periosteum to form new bone (*Trans.*, 1840, **14**, 158). Syme in spite of his many admirable qualities was frequently quarrelsome and litigious, and it is therefore both pleasing and surprising

95

when one reads in *Proceedings* (1870–71, **7**, 278) the following account of an incident in his life: 'When the late Sir David Baird was severely hurt by a kick from a horse in Berwickshire, Dr Turnbull of Coldstream who attended him, becoming somewhat anxious, brought Mr Syme to see him. Mr Syme after inspecting the broken bone, and considering the case, gave a decided opinion that there was no reasonable ground for apprehension, and returned to Edinburgh the same day. But that night Sir David Baird became restless and feverish, and Dr Turnbull, notwithstanding Syme's opinion, on the following morning thought again of sending for Syme. Early that forenoon he was surprised to see a carriage drive up to the door, and found that Syme was in it. Dr Turnbull expressed his happiness at seeing him so soon again, but asked what had brought him back: on which Syme said, "I never closed my eyes last night, because I began to fear I had given you a wrong opinion, and I have come back to see your patient again". Syme, after another examination, satisfied himself that there was too good reason for anxiety, and intimated that he thought Sir David Baird would not recover. He died two days afterwards'.

Until about 1870 medicine was based to a considerable extent on physiology or the Institutes of Medicine as it was termed in Scotland.[23] It must be pointed out, however, that in the Scottish universities the Institutes included in addition to physiology, therapeutics and pathology and occasionally bacteriology. It is therefore not surprising that J. Hughes Bennett (1812–75), Professor of the Institutes of Medicine at Edinburgh published a paper in *Transactions* (1842, **15**, 277) entitled 'On Parasitic Vegetable Structures found growing in Living Animals' which is clearly a landmark in the history of bacteriology.

John Davy (1790–1868), Inspector General of Army Hospitals, contributed twenty-one papers to the Society, most of them physiological in nature (p. 67). A different aspect of physiology is featured in a lengthy paper by James Bell Pettigrew (1834–1908) entitled 'On the Physiology of Wings, being an Analysis of the Movements by which Flight is produced in the Insect, Bat and Bird' (*Trans.*, 1870, **26**, 321). It is an important contribution to the history of aviation. He also wrote *Design in Nature* (1908), three beautifully produced books containing a mass of information.

A physiologist of international fame was Sir Edward Sharpey-

Schafer (1850–1935) who was President and gave much time and thought to the welfare of the Society. In his early researches in London he established himself as an outstanding physiologist and histologist, who opened up new fields of study by his researches on the endocrine organs. In Edinburgh his researches covered a wide area including studies on the functions of the central nervous system, muscular contraction and chloroform anaesthesia. His method of resuscitation of the apparently drowned is well known. What is less known is that he described the method in a paper he read to the Society (*Proc.*, 1903, **25**, 39).

A remarkable Fellow was William Pulteney Alison (1790–1859), Professor of the Institutes of Medicine and later of Medicine at Edinburgh University. He was a physiologist whose belief in 'vital force' in living tissue commanded considerable attention at a period when the vitalists were engaged in a heated dispute with the mechanists. The concept of 'vital force' does not now command much favour and it is generally accepted that the behaviour of living organisms can be explained by the laws of chemistry and physics without recourse to 'vital actions' which cannot be imitated in the inorganic sphere. By 'plain everyday chemistry but complex' to use Sir Charles Sherrington's (1857–1952; Hon. F.R.S.E., 1908) words. Alison is probably better remembered for his concern for the amelioration of poverty and distress in Scotland, and his incredible attention to the sick poor was an important factor in producing the Poor Law Act of 1845. It is an interesting side-light to the social scene that Alison's demand for statutory measures to deal with the problem of poverty met strong opposition from another Fellow, the Rev. Thomas Chalmers (1780–1847), who passionately believed in voluntary measures. A delightful picture of Alison is given by Christison who describes him 'giving his sixpences to a crowd of beggars at his door in Heriot Row as he left in the morning'. A similar story is told of Sir Thomas Dick Lauder distributing pennies—a 'daily and expected dole'—to beggars awaiting him on his way to town from Grange House.

A Fellow who played an important role in establishing pathology as a scientific discipline was Sir Robert Muir (1864–1959), a pioneer in relating bacteriology to medicine and a 'character' who greatly enjoyed the camaraderie of the Society. Under his leadership the Glasgow School of Pathology gained a world wide reputation and with James Lorrain Smith (1862–1931) he was mainly responsible for the foundation of the Pathological Society of Great Britain. Another Fellow who made a great contribution to pathology was William Smith Greenfield (1846–1919). According to Duvall and Currie 'if Bobby Muir is the father of British Pathology Greenfield is the grandfather'.[24]

Muir's appointment in 1894 as a Lecturer in Pathological Bacteriology in Edinburgh signalised the importance the University attached to Bacteriology, but it was not until 1913 that the Robert Irvine Chair of Bacteriology was founded. Robert Irvine (1839–1902) was a chemist who with Sir John Murray, as related in another place (p. 120), discovered valuable phosphate deposits in Christmas Island and as a result both made considerable fortunes. Irvine was deeply interested in the possibilities of bacteriological research and bequeathed the remainder of his estate to the founding of a Chair in Bacteriology.

The Chair of Materia Medica in Edinburgh, the oldest chair of this subject in the world, was for many years (1832–77) held by Sir Robert Christison (1797–1882), a polymath—botanist, chemist, mineralogist, archaeologist and pharmacologist. His $55\frac{1}{2}$ years as professor covered a period in which major contributions to medicine were made by Fellows including Gregory (morphia), Goodsir (cell theory), Hughes Bennett (leucocythaemia), Simpson (chloroform) and Lister (antisepsis). His many-sided activities included publication of his authoritative book *Treatise on Poisons* (1829), and with T. S. Traill (1781–1862), the final edition of the *Edinburgh Pharmacopoeia* (1841), based on earlier editions edited by Joseph Black, William Cullen, Andrew Duncan and others. This paved the way for the publication of the first *Pharmacopoeia of Great Britain and Ireland* (1864). Among Christison's pharmacological discoveries was the isolation and physiological action of coniine, the active principle of hemlock, and this constitutes one of the earliest investigations on the chemistry of the alkaloids and pharmacological experiments in this country (*Trans.*, 1836, **13**, 383). This was followed by the pioneer work of Crum Brown and Sir Thomas R. Fraser (1841–1920) who showed the pharmacological effects of drugs can be altered by modification of their chemical structure and thus paved the way to the science of chemotherapeutics (p. 80). The drugs used were alkaloids, substances which engaged the attention of Fellows over a long period of years (p. 119). Fraser made many notable contributions in the alkaloid field including work with Christison on physostigmine; the chemistry, pharmacology, and botany of strophanthidin (*Trans.*, 1890, **35**, 955; 1891, **36**, 343); the introduction of eserine and strophanthidin into medicine; and the antagonism of eserine and atrophine. His researches on snake poisons and immunisation against them are noteworthy for they were carried out at a time when immunisation was little understood.

Joseph Lister (1827–1912) did not make many contributions to the Society, but his paper 'On the Germ Theory of Putrefactions and other Fermentative Changes' (*Trans.*, 1872–76, **27**, 313), for which he was awarded the Makdougall Brisbane Prize, reminded the audience of his famous papers in the *Lancet* six years previously. Lister succinctly summed up his own work: 'The philosophical investigations of Pasteur long since made me a convert to the Germ Theory and it was on the basis of that theory that I founded the Theory of the antiseptic treatment of wounds in surgery'. Nearly twenty years later it fell to Lister, representing the Royal Societies of London and of Edinburgh at the celebrations in the Sorbonne of Pasteur's 70th birthday, to convey to the great Frenchman the greetings and good wishes of his countrymen. Amid scenes of unparalleled enthusiasm Pasteur, deeply moved, rose from his seat and embraced Lister: surely one of the most dramatic moments in the history of science. An interesting footnote is the fact that Lister's attention to Pasteur's epochmaking paper on 'living ferments' in *Comptes Rendus* (29 June 1863) was drawn by Thomas Anderson (1819–74), Professor of Chemistry in the University of Glasgow and author of many papers on organic chemistry in *Transactions*.

Sad to say one of Lister's bitter opponents was James Y. Simpson, who regarded the antiseptic method as competing with his own acupressure treatment. Simpson is, of course, remembered for his introduction of chloroform as an anaesthetic, a discovery which not only revolutionised surgery, but like that of Lister met with considerable unreasoned and unreasonable opposition. Some idea of the boon of anaesthesia is conveyed by a poignant letter to Simpson from George Wilson (p. 119) who had a foot amputated without an anaesthetic: 'Of the agony it occasioned I will say nothing. Suffering so great as I underwent cannot be expressed in words and thus fortunately cannot be recalled. The particular pangs are now forgotten, but the black whirlwind of emotion, the horror of great darkness and the sense of desertion by God and man bordering on despair, which swept through my mind and overwhelmed my heart, I can never forget, however gladly I would do so'.

Simpson's memory was perpetuated in 1973 by an address to the Society by Mr John Shepherd entitled 'James Young Simpson and his Times'.

Another pioneer in medical science was Sir Sydney Smith (1883–1969), recognised as one of the founders of modern forensic science. His book *Mainly Murder* can only suggest the wealth of amazing information at immediate recall.

Meteorology

It is not surprising that scientists exposed to Edinburgh's notorious climate should interest themselves in the City's wind and rain. Indeed although meteorology is not mentioned in the Charter the first volume of *Transactions* contains two papers on the subject: 'The Theory of Rain' by James Hutton (p. 63) and 'Hoar Frost' by Patrick Wilson (1743–1811), Professor of Astronomy in Glasgow University. Wilson's father had earlier raised thermometers into the atmosphere by means of kites two years before Benjamin Franklin's classical experiments in 1751. This is the first recorded use of kites for meteorological purposes (see *Trans.*, 1823–26, 10, 279).

The east wind features prominently in a number of papers and addresses including two: Hutton's 'On the Periodical Winds which prevail in Britain during the Spring and Summer' and a 'Dissertation on the Causes of the Disagreeableness and Coldness of the East Wind', read but not published by George Wallace (1727–1805), advocate. Appropriately a number of meteorological observations were carried out by Playfair in Windmill Street. Many years later J. D. Forbes published his 'classic memoir' entitled 'On the Climate of Edinburgh for 56 years, from 1795–1850' (*Trans.*, 1857–61, 22, 327), and R. C. Mossman (1870–1940), among his many meteorological papers, included three lengthy memoirs on the Edinburgh weather (*Trans.*, 1895, 38, 681; 1896, 39, 63; 1902, 40, 469). Brewster and Kelvin also contributed meteorological papers to the Society and outstanding observational work was done at Makerstoun (1841–46) by Sir Thomas Makdougall Brisbane and John Allan Broun (p. 42).

A dominating figure in Scottish meteorology was the polymath, Dr Alexander Buchan (1829–1907), perhaps most widely known today because of his 'Buchan cold spells'. His reputation rests, however, on his many contributions to our Society and elsewhere, and his paper on the 'Mean Pressure of the Atmosphere and the Prevailing Winds over the Globe' (*Trans.*, 1869, **25**, 575) was described by Hann as 'epoch-making'. Buchan mapped the isobars and isotherms of the world and showed that 'weather travels', a fact on which weather forecasting as we now know it is based. He took an active part in the appeal by the Scottish Meteorological Society, of which he was Secretary for 50 years, in raising money to build observatories at the top (1883–1904) and foot (1890–1904) of Ben Nevis. The suggestion to erect these observatories had been made by a number of men including a President and Vice-President of the R.S.E., Thomas Stevenson and David Milne Home respectively. Management of the Observatories was undertaken by the Scottish Meteorological Society along with representatives of the Royal Society of London, the Royal Society of Edinburgh and the Philosophical Society of Glasgow. In 1883 Dr R. T. Omond (1858–1914) went into residence as Director (for accounts of the work of the observatories see James Paton, *Weather*, 1954, **9**, 291; W. T. Kilgour in his book *Twenty Years on Ben Nevis*). Certain initial legal difficulties were overcome by the Royal Society of Edinburgh holding the feudal title of the acre at the top of the Ben, an undertaking sanctioned by the Royal Charter entitling the Society to hold heritable property for scientific purposes. The part played by the Society in the venture was further increased by the publication of the observations compiled by Drs Omond, Buchan, Mossman and others (*Trans.*, **34, 42, 43,** and **44**). Typical of these is Dr J. Y. Buchanan's paper 'The Meteorology of Ben Nevis in Clear and in foggy Weather' (*Trans.*, 1899, **39**, 779).

There can be no doubt that the Ben Nevis project attracted a number of eminent scientists led by the cheerful and courageous Dr Omond. Not the least remarkable was C. T. R. Wilson (1869–1959) who recorded that when on the Ben in September 1894 'The wonderful phenomena shown when the sun shone on the clouds surrounding the hilltop and especially the coloured rings surrounding the sun (coronas) or surrounding the shadow cast by the hill-top or observer on mist or clouds (glories) greatly excited my interest and made me wish to imitate them in the laboratory'. Wilson's investigations showed that clouds can be formed in the absence of dust particles and led him to the invention known as the cloud chamber, which most surprisingly arrived just in time to play a key role in Lord Rutherford's work on radioactivity and atomic structure. Rutherford described the cloud chamber as 'the most original and wonderful instrument in scientific history'. The cloud chamber, originally of the string and sealing-wax class, still plays the vital part in the multi-million pound, astonishing, nay bewildering, investigations of nuclear structure at CERN and other centres.

The cloud effects which so excited Wilson also interested Tait who encouraged Omond 'to take every opportunity of observing what are called glories'. As a result Omond produced two interesting papers on 'Glories, Halos and Coronas' (*Proc.*, 1884–86, **13**, 500).

Clouds of a different kind were the subject of investigations by John Aitken (1839–1919), who published many papers on a variety of topics, particularly on the effect of dust in the atmosphere on the formation of fogs and clouds (see especially his great papers in *Trans.*, 1881, **30**, 337; 1885, **32**, 239).[25] It is perhaps not generally known that Aitken carried out his experiments in a room in his house in Falkirk. He was a 'singularly modest' man who would never allow himself to be nominated to the office of President or Vice-President of the Society.

Meteorology in Scotland owes much to the genial and lovable James Paton (1903–73), who in 1945 successfully introduced an undergraduate course in meteorology in Edinburgh University: the first such course at a British university. This was followed in 1964 by the establishment of an independent Department of Meteorology with Paton in charge. He had a deep interest in upper-atmosphere phenomena and was greatly helped in his research by volunteers in different parts of the country.

In the early days of the Society wind was the subject of two addresses (p. 100) and a recent symposium entitled 'Wind and its Effects on Man, Plants, and Animals', organised in conjunction with the Royal Meteorological Society in 1982, is a reminder of the Society's continuing interest in meteorology.

Natural History

In the early days of the Society, Natural History according to John Walker consisted of six branches of science: 1. Meteorology; 2. Hydrography; 3. Geology; 4. Mineralogy; 5. Botany; 6. Zoology. Even in these days, however, polymaths had to select and specialise. Jameson, for example, concentrated on mineralogy, geology and zoology (p. 87), while Edward Forbes, whose main interests were botany and zoology, also worked intensively for a period on geology. Walker's broadly based definition of natural history obtained for many years, but, with the growth of knowledge, specialisation became inevitable and each of the items in his list is now a separate discipline to which others have been added. None the less the term Natural History has its uses. The Department of Natural History in Edinburgh University, for example, was renamed the Department of Zoology when it moved to its new site at King's Buildings, but one of the professors still 'professes' Natural History, while his colleague occupies the Chair of Zoology.

Of the earlier workers in the field John Walker (p. 3) and Robert Jameson have already been mentioned. Jameson was followed in the Edinburgh Chair by Edward Forbes, whose various activities included dredging expeditions in the Firth of Forth in which he obtained many marine animals and plants. He thus opened up a new field of knowledge in which one of his successors in the Edinburgh Chair of Natural History, Wyville Thomson, later carried out researches on which the science of oceanography is based (p. 112). Thomson is remembered particularly for his achievements in planning and leading the 'Challenger' and other expeditions (p. 114). Later explorers include Sir (Charles) Maurice Yonge, President of the Society (1970–73), who led the British Expedition to the Great Barrier Reef (1928), 'the most impressive coral formation in the world'.

A great individualist who served on Council for 29 years including the Presidency (1934–39) was D'Arcy Wentworth Thompson (1860–1948), a brilliant teacher, who, although he founded no research school, enjoyed an international reputation. He was a member of Dr Clyde's class at Edinburgh Academy with W. Abbot Herdman (1858–1924), D. Noel Paton and J. S. Haldane as classmates, all subsequently Fellows of the Society.[26]

The indebtedness of the Society to the Academy is further emphasised by the fact that Clerk Maxwell, Tait and Fleeming Jenkin were Edinburgh Academicals as are at the present time the Chairman and the Secretary of the Carnegie Trust for the Universities of Scotland (p. 155). D'Arcy Thompson was Professor at Dundee and St Andrews for 64 years, a remarkable achievement, and his first book contained a preface by Charles Darwin. He bridged a gap in the history of zoology and demonstrated that mathematics and physics can very profitably be applied to problems of anatomy. His great work was his book *Growth and Form* (1917), described as 'the finest piece of scientific literature in the language'. The impact of the first edition was lessened by the incredible restriction of the publication to 400 copies. It was many years before the second edition appeared (1942) by which time the price of a copy of the first edition had risen to eight times that of the original. D'Arcy's keen interest in the Society is testified by his Address in 1934 entitled 'Fifty Years Ago, in the Royal Society of Edinburgh' (*Proc.*, 1933–34, **54**, 145). His memory was later recalled by a lecture entitled 'The World of D'Arcy Wentworth Thomson revisited' by Dr P. Sprent (F.R.S.E., 1973) on 8 June 1970. A fifty year survey of a different type is to be found in Sir Maurice Yonge's (F.R.S.E., 1945) 'Molluscs and Coral Reefs' (*Trans.*, 1973–76, **69**, 147).

A naturalist who served for a long period (24 years) as a Councillor, a Secretary to the Ordinary Meetings, Vice-President and finally President was James Ritchie, who held Chairs of Natural History in Aberdeen and Edinburgh. Sir Maurice Yonge said of him that 'no-one in his generation has done more to interpret the natural history of his country'. His book *The Influence of Man on Animal Life in Scotland: a Study of Faunal Evolution* brought him international recognition. His collection of Hydroids was extensive and was catalogued by W. J. Rees and Sarah Thursfield (*Proc.*, 1963–64, **69B**, 34).[27] Professor Ritchie had a masterly command of the English language and his papers and articles are a joy to read. He was also a gifted artist and one of his pleasing water-colour landscapes hangs in the Society's house. Other Fellows who merit mention as artists are Edward Forbes (p. 113), whose sketches of the Edinburgh scene are well known: Piazzi Smyth, whose sketches in colour or black and white may be seen in his note-books: and Robert Kaye Greville (1794–1866), a well-known botanist who exhibited at the Royal Scottish Academy. The most famous of the Society's artists in the natural history field was the American naturalist, John James Audubon (1785–1851; Hon. F.R.S.E., 1827), whose *Birds of America* is a classic. The first ten plates for this book were engraved in Edinburgh by W. N. Lizars. Other artists are mentioned in the present text.

Fresh ground was broken by J. Cossar Ewart (1851–1933) with his animal breeding experiments which introduced scientific methodology into the study of heredity. Further developments in this subject came in 1920 with the formation of the Animal Breeding Research Department in Edinburgh University and the College of Agriculture with the forceful Dr F. A. E. Crew (1886–1973) as Director. Crew later became Professor of Animal Genetics and built up an important research school with the able collaboration of Alan Greenwood (1898–1981), Charlotte Auerbach and Alick Buchanan Smith, later Lord Balerno. Many communications from the Department were published in *Transactions* and *Proceedings*.

Crew was followed by Conrad Hal Waddington (1905–75), a biologist with a great breadth of knowledge and interests. He was a prolific writer and in addition to a number of books wrote nearly 500 papers and articles on a variety of topics.

Natural history covers such a wide field of topics that it is impossible to deal adequately with the contributions to the Society in the subject. Suffice to say that a regular flow of papers has come from the pens of R. A. Beatty (F.R.S.E., 1963; Keith Prizeman, 1959–61), Fabius Gross (1906–50); W. Black (1903–75; Makdougall Brisbane Prizeman, 1944–46), R. A. R. Gresson (F.R.S.E., 1942); P. C. Koller (1904–79; David Anderson Berry Prizeman, 1947) and many others.

Ornithology does not feature much in the Society's transactions, but many of the Fellows have made major contributions to the science. William Macgillivray (1796–1852) wrote a famous book *History of British Birds* and was highly regarded by Audubon. Later W. Eagle Clarke (1853–1938) wrote the authoritative *Studies in Bird Migration*. His collection of British birds was donated to the Royal Scottish Museum. Some of Eagle Clarke's views were later shown by James Ritchie to require emendation (*Proc.*, 1939–40, **60**, 299).

No one has done more to promote interest in Scottish bird life than George Waterston (1911–80). He made history by purchasing Fair Isle in 1948 and founded there a bird observatory which has gained international fame and is now in the possession of the National Trust. Waterston is also widely known as the key figure in the re-establishment of the osprey as a breeding bird in Scotland. Another Scotsman with a deep interest in natural history is Lord Home of the Hirsel (F.R.S.E., 1953), who as a boy could identify all the birds in the Border country by sight or sound. He has not allowed his busy political career to lessen his interest in natural history and his estate at the Hirsel teems with interest and has become a Mecca for naturalists. How many politicians in June of each year enjoy the pleasure of looking into boxes of nesting swifts and handling them when they are quiet? It is noteworthy that the swift nesting-boxes at the Hirsel interested another Fellow, His Royal Highness the Duke of Edinburgh, who later installed 25 similar boxes on the Terrace at Windsor Castle.

Recent recognition of ornithology by the Society was testified by awards of the Neill Prize to D. Nethersole-Thompson and the Makdougall Brisbane Prize to Andrew Rodger Waterston (F.R.S.E., 1946). A third member of the Waterston clan to figure in the Society's list of prizemen is Charles Dewar Waterston who was awarded the Keith Prize (1969–71) for his work in palaeontology.

Natural Philosophy—Physics

The nineteenth century witnessed an unparalleled development of science, pure and applied, and it is therefore not surprising that many Scottish scientists during this period devoted their energies to physics. One thinks of Brewster's long series of investigations (p. 43) and of those of many other Fellows such as Kelvin, Clerk Maxwell and Tait whose papers are to be found in *Transactions* and *Proceedings*. The contributions of these and other physicists have been dealt with already in the text and we here outline the distinguished work of other Fellows which has not been mentioned.

It may be noted that there is some justification for including Natural Philosophy in the chapter heading. The great Kelvin disliked the words *physicist* and *scientist*, and regarded himself as a *natural philosopher*.[28] It is scarcely necessary to add that he was also an extremely successful engineer.

Energy, particularly in the form of heat, was a prominent feature of the work and researches of Black, Watt, Hutton, Hall and other Fathers of the Society and continued to be a dominant feature of the researches of many Fellows throughout the nineteenth century. This is scarcely surprising in a period which included the fruitful years 1840–70 in which the conservation of energy was propounded by Mayer and Joule (p. 68). Sir John Leslie (1766–1832), Professor of Mathematics (1805–19) and later of Natural Philosophy (1819–33) in Edinburgh did not contribute many papers to the Society although when his first paper in *Transactions* (1785–89, 2, 193) appeared he was only 22 years of age. One of his experiments is famous. He showed that water when boiled at a low pressure cools and freezes. In other words it freezes in the act of boiling! It is essential for the success of the experiment that the vacuum in which the evaporation is being effected be dry, and Leslie ensured this by using roasted oatmeal, an indication of the limited resources at his command. He established for himself an enviable reputation not only for his experimental skill, but also by the publication of 'An Experimental Inquiry into the Nature and Propagation of Heat' which appeared in 1804. Leslie's career was not devoid of incident. An accusation that he was an atheist nearly cost him the appointment of Professor of Mathematics and he ran into trouble when in 1826 he introduced in the University a new series of lectures for mixed classes of ladies and gentlemen. According to Sir Alexander Grant (1826–84): 'unseemly results are said to have followed' and the Senatus regarded the innovation as unworthy of the dignity of the University. The Town Council permitted a course for one year, but after that it was dropped. Another episode is recalled by Robert Louis Stevenson in *College Papers*. 'There appeared in *Lapsus Linguae* or the *College Tatler* [a student] paper a most bitter satire upon Sir John Leslie, in which he was compared to Falstaff, charged with puffing himself and very prettily censured for publishing the first volume of a class-book, and making all purchasers pay for both. Sir John took up the matter angrily, and threatened the publisher [of *Lapsus*] with an action, till he was forced to turn the hapless *Lapsus* out of doors'.

Leslie's successor in the Chair of Natural Philosophy (1833–59) was James David Forbes (p. 45) and another profound physicist of the period was W. J. MacQuorn Rankine (1820–72), Professor of Engineering in Glasgow University, who in a paper to the Society on the mechanical action of heat (*Trans.*, 1850, **20**, 147, 561) deduced the second law of thermodynamics. He also introduced the term *potential energy* to contrast this form of energy with that of *kinetic energy*, subsequently coined by Tait and Thomson. He generalised the notion of energy and with Clausius and Kelvin laid the foundations of thermodynamics. Macquorn Rankine was both profound and industrious, but the several notices about him stress also his genial and extrovert character. One commented on 'the amiability of his temper and the warmth of his affections'. He composed amusing verses one of which may be quoted here. It is taken from a poem written when Sir William Thomson (later Lord Kelvin) was trying to win his students to the metric system.

> Some talk of millilitres and some of kilogrammes,
> And some of decilitres, to measure beer and drams:
> But I'm a British workman, too old to go to school,
> So by pounds I'll eat, and by quarts I'll drink
> And I'll work by my three-foot rule.

Lord Kelvin's contribution to physics is, of course, legendary (p. 47), but less well known was his brother James (1822–92) who made the important and interesting prediction that the freezing-point of water would be lowered by pressure (*Trans.*, 1849, **16**, 575): a prediction later verified by Kelvin.

One of Edinburgh's most brilliant sons, James Clerk Maxwell (1831–79), a schoolboy, used to attend meetings of the Society (p. 15). At the age of 15 he submitted a paper to the Society 'On the Description of Oval Curves and those having a Plurality of Foci', which was read by James D. Forbes (*Proc.*, 1846, **2**, 89) and three years later another of his papers was read, this time by Kelland. It apparently was felt unacceptable that the Society should be addressed by a schoolboy. Others who have read papers to the Society while still in their teens include Robert Broom (1866–1951, Hon. F.R.S.E., 1947), who at the age of 18 seems to have been permitted to deliver the paper in person (*Proc.*, 1884–85, **13**, 72). Clerk Maxwell published other papers including one on

Experiments on Colour, as perceived by the Eye, with Remarks on Colour-Blindness (*Trans.*, 1853–57, **21**, 275) described by Tolstoy[29] as his first major paper. His first paper and Forbes' report as referee on it are now treasured exhibits in the Society's museum. It is noteworthy that as Cargill Knott points out: 'Maxwell passed on to Cambridge with a vast amount of learning which the pedantic mathematical tutor regarded as useless lumber for one aiming at a high Wranglership'. Maxwell's subsequent contributions to science are now part of history with his comprehensive electromagnetic theory of light leading on the practical side to radio communication and on the theoretical side to relativity. Not everyone recognised the significance of Clerk Maxwell's work, but Tait had no doubt about it and refers in his obituary notice to 'the imperishable writings of Clerk Maxwell'.[30]

A plaque at 14 India Street, Edinburgh, marks Maxwell's birthplace and the centenary of his death was commemorated in the Society's rooms on 12 November 1979 by an address by Professor William Cochran (F.R.S.E., 1965) and a Service in Corsock Parish Church when a message from the Society was read by Professor J. C. Gunn (F.R.S.E., 1959). An account of Clerk Maxwell's life and work by Professor R. V. Jones (F.R.S.E., 1949) is given in the *Year Book*, 1980, 5.

An Edinburgh optician, William Nicol (1766–1851) invented a prism which generates plane polarised light and is the main component in the polarimeter, an instrument of capital importance in the history of stereochemistry.[31] The first polarimeter was constructed by E. Mitscherlich in 1844, the year in which he published his paper on sodium ammonium racemate which led Pasteur to effect the first resolution of a racemic compound into its optically active components. The Royal Scottish Museum possesses a prism made by Nicol in his eightieth year.

The theory of the Nicol prism was the subject of a paper by Edward Sang (1805–90), who regarded his theory as 'one of his chief contributions to science'. Unfortunately, the paper was mislaid in the Society's office and saw the light of day fifty-four years later when it was resurrected by Tait at Sang's urgent request shortly before his death (*Proc.*, 1891, **18**, 323, 337). Sang, however, is best known for his book *The New General Theory of the Teeth of Wheels*, a recognised classic on the subject. Much of his life was devoted to the compilation of logarithmic tables and included the mammoth task of calculating seven-place logarithmic tables of all numbers up to 200,000 and logarithms up to 15 places between 100,000 and 370,000 (see Cargill Knott's article on 'Edward Sang and his Logarithmic Calculations' in the *Napier Memorial Volume*, 1915). Sang's work is surely unique as an example of persistence and endurance, and would nowadays be done by computer.

The belated publication of Sang's paper on the Nicol Prism recalls two other unfortunate Scotsmen—Scott Couper (p. 18) and John James Waterston. The latter in 1846 submitted a paper to the Royal Society of London entitled 'On the Physics of Media which are composed of Free and Perfectly Elastic Molecules in a State of Motion'. The bold propositions contained in this paper failed to convince the referees, one of whom gave it as his considered opinion that 'the paper is nothing but nonsense, unfit even for reading before the Society'. As a result it lay in the Royal Society's archives until it was unearthed by Lord Rayleigh (1842–1919; Hon. F.R.S.E., 1886) who caused it to be published in the *Philosophical Transactions*, 1892, **183**, 1 (J. S. Haldane, *The Collected Papers of J. J. Waterston*, 1928). Waterston's theory which postulates that the pressure of a gas depends on the kinetic energy of the molecules and their concentration was later enunciated by Clerk Maxwell in the law of equipartition of kinetic energy among the molecules of a gas. Neglect of Waterston's paper might have been avoided had he been a Fellow of the Edinburgh Society with the opportunity thus afforded of discussing scientific problems at meetings or in conversation with men such as Kelvin or Brewster.

A student of and assistant to James D. Forbes was Balfour Stewart who spent most of his working life in England. During his Edinburgh period he wrote two important papers (*Trans.*, 1857–61, **22**, 1, 59) on radiant heat and the spectra thus produced: 'the product of a mind lit by a spark in Forbes's workshop'. Also interested in spectrum analysis was William Swan (1818–94), Professor of Natural Philosophy at St Andrews University, who showed in a paper entitled 'The Prismatic Spectra of the Flames of Compounds of Hydrogen and Carbon' (*Trans.*, 1857, **21**, 411) that the yellow line in the spectrum is due to sodium. Swan invented a prism photometer (*Trans.*, 1849, **16**, 581), which is essentially the same as that of Lummer and Brod-

Professor Balfour among the Neeps.

J. Hutton Balfour

Sir David Brewster

Alexander Crum Brown

Professor CHR-ST-L,
who recently succeeded, amid a scene of unrivalled enthusiasm,
in making a correct addition.

George Chrystal

The "SOCIETY OF ARTS FOR SCOTLAND" (now The Royal Scottish Society of Arts) met in the Royal Institution, Princes Street, when that building was erected in 1826 and for several years thereafter.

Royal Institution, Princes Street, Edinburgh

Old College Library, Edinburgh

VIEW down GLENGLUOY from the hills at its upper extremity from point *a* in the map.

a. Ben Nevis seen at a distance.   b. Bank of the Gluoy.

Parallel Roads of Glen Roy

First Schools' Christmas Lecture, 1980

hun, constructed forty years later. Cargill Knott (*Proc.*, 1899–1900, **23**, 12) directed attention to this fact and commented that 'it was no small astonishment that such an important contribution to knowledge should have escaped the notice of the myriad of workers in photometry'.

Sir James Dewar (1842–1923), Professor of Natural Philosophy in Cambridge, and of Chemistry in the Royal Institution, discovered while still in Edinburgh the use of charcoal in the production of high vacua and thereby opened up the field of liquefaction of gases and the production of low temperatures. His vacuum flasks are, of course, in everyday use. He made notable discoveries in chemistry (p. 80) and with J. G. M'Kendrick (1841–1926), Professor of the Institutes of Medicine in Glasgow, carried out pioneer work on the physiological action of light (*Trans.*, 1872–76, **27**, 141).

For the greater part of the nineteenth century atoms were the business of the chemist (p. 65), but in the last years of the century physicists turned their attention to nuclear physics and effected a revolutionary change in the course of a few years (1885–1915). The discoveries of Röntgen, J. J. Thomson, the Curies, Rutherford and others on the experimental side and of Einstein and Planck on the theoretical side brought an unparalleled addition to our knowledge of the properties of matter which completely altered the sciences of physics and chemistry. It is disappointing to discover that the Society appears to have been little concerned with the epoch-making events occurring in the Cavendish Laboratory and elsewhere. Except for the election of J. J. Thomson to Honorary Fellowship in 1905 the Society stolidly continued its rather conservative programme with emphasis on geology, mathematics and biology. It is difficult to understand why the 'life and undertakings' of the Society at this period should be so orthodox and slightly colourless especially when it is remembered that for twelve of these momentous years Kelvin was President.[32] It is tempting to speculate on what might have been had Rutherford's application for the Chair on Tait's death been successful. Later the situation, as least as far as physics is concerned, was rectified by the inclusion in the Fellowship of Sir Charles G. Darwin, Sir Edward Appleton, Norman Feather, Max Born and others.

In 1892 Edinburgh University with commendable foresight

instituted a lectureship in Applied Mathematics and Cargill G. Knott (p. 49) held it with distinction for some 30 years. Later the lecturership was changed to the Tait Chair of Mathematical Physics which was first occupied (1923–36) by Sir Charles G. Darwin, later Director of the National Physical Laboratory, and then by Nobel Prizeman, Max Born (1882–1970), who built up in Edinburgh a school of higher studies and research in physics. All three were R. S. E. Prizemen. Born had as a member of his staff Robert Schlapp (F.R.S.E., 1927; Curator, 1959–69) and was succeeded in the Chair by Nicholas Kemmer (F.R.S.E., 1954).

That the great advances in nuclear physics made since 1964 have not suffered the neglect of those at the beginning of the century was evidenced by a survey given by Professor I. S. Hughes (F.R.S.E., 1974) in a lecture to the Society (11 January 1982) entitled 'New Particles in Physics'.

The good example set by Principal Sir David Brewster has been followed by his successors at Edinburgh University, all of whom have taken a lively interest in the Society's activities (see, e.g. p. 48).[33] One of them, Sir Alfred Ewing (1855–1935), began his career as a physicist under Tait and gained wide recognition from his later work on magnetic hysteresis. His book *Magnetic Induction in Iron and Other Metals* was regarded as a classic. Another Principal who, in spite of the heavy demands of University administration, continued to take an active interest in scientific research was Nobel Prizeman Sir Edward Appleton (1893–1965; Hon. F.R.S.E., 1947). In his later years with the help of a personal assistant he engaged in theoretical analysis and to the end of his life was in correspondence with other workers in his chosen field. Appleton is best known for his discovery of electrically conducting layers in the earth's upper atmosphere and the demonstration that there are two layers in the ionosphere, one of which is known as the Appleton layer. It is interesting that the postulation of electrical currents circulating in the upper atmosphere and thus causing the diurnal variations of the earth's magnetism had been made in 1882 by Balfour Stewart (1828–87).

Oceanography

'Oceanography is the science of the sea in all aspects, and Edinburgh is the birthplace and home of modern oceanography'. So wrote in 1921 W. A. Herdman, Professor of Oceanography in the University of Liverpool, and he singled out for special mention three notable men who had made outstanding contributions to the development of the science: Edward Forbes, Wyville Thomson and John Murray. He might have included a fourth, John Walker (p. 3), who among his many activities included the examination of the bed of the Firth of Forth by dredging.

Edward Forbes in a short life produced an amazing quantity of first-rate work in marine biology and his books *British Starfishes* (1841) and *British Molluscs* (1853) are classics. He spent many vacations exploring the bottom of the sea and his observations led to the 'Challenger' and other expeditions. Much of his work had geological significance and he brought his zoological knowledge of the animals he had to deal with as fossils to bear on geological problems. His paper 'On the Connection between the Distribution of the existing Fauna and Flora of the British Isles and the Geological Changes which have affected their Area' (*Mem. Geol. Surv.*, 1846, 1) has also been described as classic. Tragically he died some six months after attaining the Chair of Natural History in the University of Edinburgh. In addition to his intellectual gifts Forbes was a man of extraordinary charm and was an artist as well as a scientist (p. 104). His early caricatures of his professors are amusing as are his pointed comments on them. Of Monro *tertius* (1773–1859), for example, he said: 'He was parsimonious in knowledge as well as cash, although abounding in both'.

It is interesting to note that Forbes was one of a number of workers in this and related fields who for a variety of reasons left the University without completing the medical course. Others include Robert Jameson, Charles Darwin, Wyville Thomson, John Murray, William Speirs Bruce, Charles Bell and D'Arcy Thompson.

On evidence which later proved to be insufficient Forbes placed the zero of life in the ocean at about 300 fathoms and it was left to Wyville Thomson in 1869 to show that this was a gross underestimate by obtaining evidence of a great variety of living beings at the enormous depth of 2435 fathoms. It is interesting that Fleeming Jenkin while repairing a cable in the Mediterranean some years previously detected sessile animals attached to the broken cable at a depth greater than 1000 fathoms.

Sir Wyville Thomson (1830–82) was forced by ill-health after three years as a medical student to give up all thoughts of the medical profession, and returned to his first love, natural history. His ability was early recognised and in 1870 he succeeded Allman as Professor of Natural History at the University of Edinburgh. Previous to this he had organised two successful expeditions in Admiralty surveying steamers which enabled him to explore the depths of the sea and his book *The Depths of the Sea* (1872) is the first text-book of oceanography. The success of these expeditions led to his appointment as planner and leader of the 'Challenger' Expedition (1872–76)—one of the greatest scientific explorations of the seas ever undertaken. The expedition, organised by the Royal Society of Edinburgh, Edinburgh University and the Royal Navy, with the Society acting as publication medium, was a monumental voyage of some 69,000 nautical miles in 1,000 days at sea. The expedition greatly added to our knowledge of currents and temperatures of the oceans, the geology and biology of the sea-beds, and animal life in abyssal waters. To catalogue and investigate the enormous collection of specimens, which had been gathered and to arrange for publishing the results was the task set the 'Challenger' Expedition Commission, under the Directorship of Wyville Thomson. Under such a heavy load of work and responsibility Wyville Thomson's health failed and in 1881 he resigned the Directorship and died the following year. He did succeed, however, in giving a preliminary account of the Expedition in *The Voyage of the 'Challenger'* (*The Atlantic*) and he reached the important conclusion: 'It would seem that the enormous pressure, the utter darkness, and the differences of the chemical and physical conditions of the water and in the proportion of its contained gases depending on such extreme conditions, do not influence life to any great extent'.

Wyville Thomson was succeeded as Director by (later Sir) John Murray (1841–1914), who had greatly assisted him on the 'Challenger' expedition. Murray had begun his expeditionary activities as surgeon on a Peterhead trawler in the Arctic after claiming that rank because of his few weeks as a medical student in Edinburgh. He edited the fifty large volumes of the 'Challenger' series of Reports, which record 'the greatest advance in our knowledge of our planet since the great geographical discoveries of the fifteenth and sixteenth centuries'. Seven of the

Reports were written largely or entirely by himself and include the monumental 'Deep-Sea Deposits of the Atlantic Ocean' (with James Chumley (1861–1948), *Trans.*, 1923–26, **54**, 1–252). The series was claimed to be 'the longest scientific publication ever issued by any country or age', but the claim cannot be sustained since more than a century earlier Nevil Maskelyne (1732–1811) superintended the publication of 'Astronomical Observations made at the Royal Observatory, Greenwich' (1767–1815) in 50 volumes. Maskelyne, it may be noted, is remembered in Scotland for his experiments on gravity carried out on the slopes of Schiehallion (1774), as a result of which he was awarded the Copley medal of the Royal Society of London for 'his curious and laborious observations on the attraction of mountains'.

The centenary of the 'Challenger' expedition was celebrated in Edinburgh, 12–20 September 1972, at the Second International Congress on the History of Oceanography, organised by the Royal Societies of London and of Edinburgh, the City and University of Edinburgh (*Proc.*, 1972, **72–73B**) and opened by an Address from Sir Maurice Yonge on the 'Inception and Significance of the "Challenger" Expedition' (*Proc.*, 1972, **72B**, 1).

The three pioneers—Forbes, the dredger of shallow waters; Wyville Thomson, the explorer of the deep seas; and John Murray, a born leader of men 'who may be regarded as the founder of the post-"Challenger" oceanography'—were followed by another outstanding explorer, William Speirs Bruce (1867–1921), who made a number of expeditions to the polar regions and led the 'Scotia' Scottish National Antarctic Expedition (1902–04). The scientific results were published in some 30 memoirs (*Trans.*, 1904–20) and constituted a major contribution to Antarctic oceanography. A characteristic of Bruce's 'Scotia' expedition is that the results were obtained at a cost of £35,000 compared to Scott's 'Discovery' expedition at a cost of £350,000. In the course of his expeditions Bruce discovered a new part of the Antarctic continent which he named Coat's Land. He was also the first to realise the wealth of coal and minerals at Spitzbergen.

During her voyage *Scotia* liberated drift bottles, one of which, having been put to sea on 1 December 1903 at Burdwood Bank was found on 7 September 1952 at North Island, New Zealand, having travelled a record 10,000 miles. Remnants of the bottle's contents are to be seen in the Society's rooms.

Second in command in Bruce's 1919 Scottish Expedition to Spitzbergen was (later Sir) James Mann Wordie (1889–1962), who had been a member of the famous Shackleton Antarctic expedition (1914). It may be recalled that the *Endurance* broke up under ice-pressure and the members of the expedition were forced to make the legendary journey on drifting ice and open boat to Elephant Island, from where Shackleton made his way to South Georgia to find a rescue ship. Shackleton's leadership was tested to the utmost and he was greatly helped by two men—Frank Wild and James Wordie. Wordie later acted as second-in-command of Bruce's Spitzbergen Expedition.

Technology

The life and soul of science is its practical application; and just as the great advances in mathematics have been made through the solution of problems which were of a highly practical kind in mathematical science, so in physical science many of the greatest advances that have been made from the beginning of the world to the present time have been made in the earnest desire to turn the knowledge of the properties of matter to some purpose useful to mankind.

Lord Kelvin

The interplay between science and technology, between pure and applied science, is a fascinating and reciprocal process. The benefits science derives from technology are very clearly outlined by Count Rumford's observation during his famous cannon-boring experiments that 'very interesting philosophical experiments may often be made without trouble or expense by means of machinery contrived for the mere mechanical arts and manufactures'. On the other hand Clerk Maxwell's theory of electricity and light leading to the great radio industry of today illustrates the impact of 'pure' science on technology.

Although the scientific activities and interests of the Society have largely been concerned with their academic aspects the technological side has never been neglected. Indeed as early as 1782 John Walker in his proposal for establishing the Royal Society of Edinburgh (p. 3) specifically referred to 'the improvement of the Agriculture, Manufacture and Fisheries of Scotland'. Other examples of the Society's interest in technology are provided by the inclusion in its Fellowship of men like James Watt

(1736–1819), a founding Fellow; John Roebuck (1718–94), also a founder member and founder of the Carron Iron Works; four generations of the Stevenson family, famed for their lighthouse construction (p. 83); and Fleeming Jenkin and Lord Kelvin who were heavily involved in the manufacture and laying down of several great telegraph cables (p. 83). On the chemical side we find James Hutton and James Davy successfully undertaking the manufacture of ammonia from soot. This enterprise incidentally had more than industrial significance for the profits, it is said, enabled Hutton to have the leisure necessary for his geological researches. More than a hundred years later Sir James Walker (p. 80) and Dr A. C. Cumming, both academics, joined with the industrial chemist John W. Romanes in answering their country's need by setting up a factory for the manufacture of trinitrotoluene (T.N.T.). Although complete novices in the manufacture of this explosive, the three partners succeeded in preparing it in record-breaking purity and yield. Another industrial chemist who showed his interest in the Society in a most generous manner (p. 122) was Lord Fleck, Chairman of Imperial Chemical Industries Ltd.

In the Society's *Transactions* industrial processes are discussed from time to time. Volume 5 contains a paper by John Roebuck on the management of blast furnaces, a topic which was later dealt with by Thomas Clark, Professor of Chemistry at Marischal College, Aberdeen (*Trans.*, 1833–36, **13**, 373). Technological topics have also been the subject of lectures and symposia and include two on the manufacture of cast iron by James F. W. Johnston (16 April 1832) and Robert Bald (1776–1861) (18 February 1833). Sir Alastair Pilkington's lecture on 'The Float Glass Process' (2 March 1970) and the Symposium on Energy (1 July 1974) provide more recent instances of the Society'si nterest in technology.

It is not the least of the Society's functions to provide the opportunity for Fellows and their friends to meet and engage in informal discussion and we know that such discussions have not infrequently proved to be stimulating and valuable. John Robison and Joseph Black often discussed with James Watt the application of science to engineering and as early as 1759 Robison made the prophetic suggestion to Watt that the steam engine might be used to move carriage wheels and for other purposes. It is also not difficult to imagine that latent heat was frequently a topic of conversation between Watt and his intimate friend Joseph Black. Another example of the fruitfulness of informal discussion is to be found in the magnificent series of photographs of Edinburgh and its worthies made by David Octavius Hill and Robert Adamson. The importance of the invention of the calotype photographic process by William Henry Fox Talbot was immediately appreciated in Scotland, particularly by David Brewster, a personal friend of Fox Talbot and by John Adamson, a medical practitioner who served on the St Andrews University staff and who produced a calotype in 1841. John Adamson introduced calotyping to his younger brother Robert and the stage was set for the final act. Octavius Hill, an artist, had undertaken to paint a group portrait of the 500 clergymen attending the First General Assembly of the Free Church of Scotland at which the Act of Separation and the Deed of Demission was signed at Tanfield in May 1843. Now Brewster had been one of those to sign the Act of Separation and had been present at Tanfield and he suggested to Hill that as an *aide memoire* for his enormous undertaking—the picture was completed some 20 years later—he should photograph ministers and groups of ministers and on these base his picture. Brewster further suggested that Robert Adamson would be an ideal technical assistant for Hill and thus started the happy productive partnership of Adamson and Hill. The famous picture, now hung in the office of the Free Church of Scotland on the Mound, contains portraits of three prominent Fellows—Chalmers, Brewster and Simpson as well as of Adamson and Hill.[34] It is perhaps sad that it was not until 1852 that photography was the subject of a lecture and demonstration to the Society (p. 29) by Captain Scott.

Agriculture is a subject in which Walker, Hutton and Francis Home, all Founding Members of the Society, took more than a passing interest. Sir Francis Home (1719–1813) first Professor of Materia Medica at Edinburgh University, was the author of *Principles of Agriculture and Vegetation* in which he urged the application of science to agriculture. Somewhat later Henry Stephens (1795–1874) wrote his three volumes of the *Book of the Farm* (1842–44), a fifth edition of which was still in demand in 1908. The book had an enormous circulation and was translated into many languages.

Home, it may be added, made the very useful suggestion that dilute sulphuric acid be used instead of sour milk in the bleaching process thus accomplishing in 24 hours what had previously occupied some weeks. The price of sulphuric acid had been greatly reduced by Roebuck's development of the lead chamber process and his plant at Prestonpans became the largest in the world for the manufacture of the acid.

The thriving pharmaceutical industry of Edinburgh in the nineteenth century can be traced back in part to William Gregory (1803–58),[35] Professor of Chemistry at Edinburgh University and the last of the 'Academic Gregories' to hold a Scottish Chair (p. 27). His health prevented him making the contribution to science he might otherwise have done, although it should be noted that Liebig in 1837 made no secret of his poor opinion of British chemists with two exceptions, Thomas Graham and William Gregory. Two of Gregory's papers although scientifically slight are of considerable importance. He read a paper to the Society on 'The Chemical History of Opium' and in 1831 prepared morphine hydrochloride for the first time in the pure crystalline form. This opened the way to the clinical use of the alkaloid at a time when many of the so-called morphine products contained unspecified quantities of morphine. John Fletcher Macfarlan, a surgeon apothecary who ran a pharmaceutical business in Edinburgh and did a great trade in laudanum, was so impressed by Gregory's work that by 1833 he was manufacturing morphine hydrochloride on the large scale. Another pharmacist who was impressed by Gregory's investigations was Thomas Smith who worked with his brother, and the firm T. and H. Smith began manufacturing morphine hydrochloride in 1837. The two firms for many years met a world-wide demand for pure alkaloids and when they united in 1962 the combine continued the manufacture of alkaloids as its main activity.

Gregory also published a useful paper on the preparation of pure chloroform and stressed the necessity of using only the pure compound in anaesthesia (*Proc.*, 1844–50, **2**, 316). Soon the two firms already mentioned and Messrs Duncan and Flockhart were manufacturing pure chloroform and Edinburgh became the principal source of the anaesthetic. A partner of Macfarlan, David Rennie Brown, made the important discovery (1863) that the tendency of chloroform to decompose and yield phosgene (carbonyl chloride) is prevented by the addition of a small quantity of ethyl alcohol. It may be interpolated here that phosgene was discovered by John Davy (p. 96) in the course of the chlorine controversy (p. 67).[36]

A member of Macfarlan and Co. was D. B. Dott (1852–1941) who published many papers on the opium alkaloids and was an internationally acknowledged authority in the field.

No account of chemical technology in Scotland would be complete without mention of the founder of the petroleum refining industry, James Young (1811–83). In 1847 he set up a refinery to produce illuminating and lubricating oil from a deposit in Derbyshire to which his attention had been drawn by Lyon Playfair. The spring, however, soon showed signs of failing and this led Young to seek other fields. In the event he took out a patent for the distillation of cannel coal and applied it on the industrial scale at Bathgate. The supply of cannel coal proved to be limited and Young turned to oil-bearing shale which he showed yields lubricants and 'naphtha', the latter yielding on distillation paraffin oil. He set up the successful shale oil industry in West Lothian some three years before Drake's discovery of petroleum in America. Young was not only an industrial entrepreneur, but also one with a pronounced scientific bent and he carried out experiments to determine the velocity of light.

Chance and circumstance often play an important role in the industrial application of science, and as one of the Society's Vice-Presidents, David Milne Home, stated: 'Most of these contrivances and processes, such as electro-magnetism, electro-plating, photography, artificial light, improved telescopes and microscopes, anaesthetical agents or medical disinfectants, sprung out of experiments, observations or speculations, were very unpromising as regards any practical utility when first announced, but ultimately became sources of incredible wealth, as well as of vastly increased comfort and enjoyment'. It is unlikely that Simpson, for example, realised the considerable commercial implications for the Capital of his discovery of chloroform as an anaesthetic. Chance too played a part in leading the 'Challenger' (p. 98) to the regions adjacent to the island of Java where the collection of some pieces of phosphate led to the discovery of the phosphate deposits of Christmas Island. Sir John Murray persuaded the British Government to annex the island and a company under Sir John's presidency developed a highly successful phosphate mine there. The Company eventually paid more in royalties than the entire cost of the 'Challenger' Expedition (p. 114).

The adoption of a scientific discovery to everyday use is frequently a lengthy process as Brewster found in 1811 when he described his Dioptric Apparatus (p. 43). One can understand Brewster's chagrin for as Brougham later pointed out by application of the invention to lighthouses 'an incalculable number of lives have been saved in the prevention of shipwrecks' and one is reminded of Humphry Davy and his safety lamp.

It must be conceded that there are always men critical of the commercial exploitation of scientific knowledge. John Waterston (p. 110), for example, was highly critical of Kelvin's engineering activities and held, like Faraday, that scientists should earn their living in ways other than by industrial application of their discoveries (p. 107). Kelvin, however, regarded himself both as a scientist and an engineer and his enthusiasm for applied science was made in a revealing remark about the Niagara Falls: 'Beautiful as that work of nature is, it would be more beautiful still if these waters fell upon turbine wheels, every one of which was turning the wheels of industry'. Sir Edward Appleton was equally emphatic: 'In short, it is as a creative individualist, who has found a happy mean between thought and action, that I would especially honour the applied scientist'. Benjamin Franklin had no doubts on the subject and his lightning conductor was the first example of the application of a knowledge of electricity to man's use.

The Society has always had a close and, for long periods, personal link with the printing and publishing trade (see, e.g. p. 59). Patrick Neill (p. 60) of the firm Messrs Neill and Co. Ltd was an active and enthusiastic Fellow and his firm were Printers to the Society from 1783–1970. As a token of their close relationship with the Society Messrs Neill and Co. Ltd in 1890 published in handsome form a *General Index of the First Thirty-Four Volumes of Transactions* (1783–1888), which contains not only a subject and author index of the contents of *Transactions* over the first hundred years of the Society's existence, but also much useful information about the Society and its history. A valuable supplement covering volumes 35–46 of *Transactions* (1889–1908) was later published by the same firm.

More recently, the Society has taken advantage of the experience and expertise of Messrs Robert Grant (1879–1959) and his son Douglas (F.R.S.E., 1949). The *Journal of Pathology* and the *Edinburgh University Journal* owe much to Robert's help and advice, and the magnificent *The Lost Drawings* (p. 34), with which the Society is proud to be associated, was 'seen through the press' by Douglas.

In the related field of cartography, the Bartholomew family is pre-eminent and 1987 should, *Deo volente*, witness a hundred years of almost unbroken Fellowship of three members of the family: John George (1860–1920; F.R.S.E., 1887), John (Ian) (1890–1962; F.R.S.E., 1921), and John (F.R.S.E., 1964). Of the firm's notable productions perhaps the most interesting from a scientific point of view were the Royal Geographical Society's *The Survey Atlas of Scotland* (1895), *The Atlas of Meteorology* (1899) and *The Atlas of Zoogeography* (1911), prepared by Dr J. G. Bartholomew with the assistance of Fellows such as Alexander Buchan, W. Eagle Clark, Percy H. Grimshaw and many others of international reputation. The maps are superb and are accompanied by authentic and comprehensive texts. John Bartholomew in 1949 read a paper to the Society on new projections to show circumpolar relationships in the northern hemisphere. This forms the basis for the production of maps for air travel.

Another well-known Edinburgh firm of cartographers is W. and A. K. Johnston which produced *The Physical Atlas of Natural Phenomena* (including geology and meteorology) in 1848. Responsible for this, the first physical atlas to be produced in Britain, was Alexander K. Johnston (1804–71), brother of Sir William Johnston, founder of the firm. It was recorded in 1885 that 'one half of all the maps produced in the world at the present day are prepared and printed in Edinburgh, the houses of Johnston and Bartholomew taking the lead'.

Cartography interested Tait and in a paper to the Society he considered the four-colour conjecture of map-makers that not more than four colours are required if a map is to contain no adjacent countries or counties having the same colour (*Proc.*, 1880, **10**, 501, 729; see also F. Guthrie, *ibid.*, p. 727).

Thanks to the generosity of the late Lord Fleck the Society's interest in technology has been strengthened by a Fund for the Promotion of Interest in Science and Technology in Scotland (p. 61). The Fund, originally given anonymously, has been applied to a number of ventures including lectures to schools and particularly for one by Professor John Lenihan (F.R.S.E., 1967) on 'The Triumph of Technology' in which tribute was paid to the 'many prophetic insights' of George Wilson (p. 73) (*Year Book,* 1980, p. 25).

The new technology, perhaps the outstanding feature of the post-war years, has been pioneered by many scientists including Fellows of the Society. Dr Robert Pringle (F.R.S.E., 1964), for example, founded Nuclear Enterprises (G.B.) Ltd and with the assistance of his brother, Derek (F.R.S.E., 1970), built up the leading company in Europe in the application of nucleonic and ultrasonic techniques to a wide range of problems including medical diagnosis, industrial process control, and geophysics. Donald McCallum (F.R.S.E., 1973), Director and General Manager, Ferranti Ltd, Scotland, has carried out research in a number of fields including computers and airborne radar, while Professor W. E. J. Farvis (F.R.S.E., 1958) with his expertise in microelectronics has dedicated his energies to bridging the university-industry gap by playing a leading role in Edinburgh University's Centre of Industrial Consultancy and Liaison and the Wolfson Micro-electronics Liaison Unit. The Society's lecture programmes also exemplify the continuing interest in technology.

Literary Class[37]

In the early days of the Society interests other than scientific were catered for by the Literary Class (p. 7). The two sections met on different dates; each published its papers separately in *Transactions*; each selected its own officers. The division into the two classes was abandoned in 1828, but a reminder of them is still found in the Council's two Secretaries to the Ordinary Meetings.

It has already been indicated (p. 8) that the affairs of the Society until recently have from the beginning been dominated by scientists, but it cannot be too strongly stressed that the Fellowship in its formative years was greatly strengthened by men of the stature of Dugald Stewart, Adam Smith, Adam Ferguson, Henry Mackenzie and Walter Scott, and the tradition thus established has been maintained ever since. Hugh Blair,[38] for example, was a Founding Member and all his successors in the Chair of Rhetoric and English Literature at Edinburgh until the end of the 19th century were, with one exception, Fellows. It must be admitted that contributions from the Literary Class have not been numerous, but as Dr Melville Clark (F.R.S.E., 1933) pointed out in his Bicentenary Tribute to Walter Scott (*Year Book*, 1971–72, 5) one was 'momentous'. In 1788 Henry Mackenzie read a paper to the Society entitled 'Account of the German Theatre' (*Trans.*, 1790, **2**, 154) and Scott in his 'Essay on Imitations of the Ancient Ballad' recalled the lecture which revealed to him the existence of the German Ballad and 'provoked him to learn German for himself, as a key to a new world of romance. He was soon "German-mad", as he said, and ramping through Goethe and Schiller. He devoured everything he could lay his hands on, and translated ballads and plays wholesale with far more zest than accuracy. The result was that the German romantics of the *Sturm und Drang* period cross-fertilised his mind. They turned him into a creative writer of them'. Scott's German studies may also have been stimulated by another Fellow, Alexander Fraser Tytler (Lord Woodhouselee, 1747–1813), Professor of Universal History at Edinburgh University.

Walter Scott (1771–1832) became a Fellow in 1800 and was elected to the Presidency in 1820, a position he held to his death. He enjoyed his leadership of the Society—'My Presidency (of the Royal Society of Edinburgh) took place with great eclat' he wrote and he was doubtless both amused and gratified when a Leipzig bookseller, writing to Scott, on 20 November 1826, addressed his letter:

To
Sir Walter Scott Esquire,
Lord of Abbotsford and President
of the Academy of Sciences at
Edinburgh.

Until financial disaster and ill-health overtook him he took an active part in the Society's affairs (see, e.g. p. 71). His popularity is evidenced by a sad entry in his wonderful *Journal* for 17 January 1826, the day after he 'came through cold roads to as cold news'. The entry reads: 'Have apologised (for not) attending the Royal Society Club, who have a *Gaudeamus* on this day, and seem'd to count much on my being Praeses'. It is of interest that in 1939 John Guthrie Tait (1861–1945), the eldest son of Peter

Guthrie Tait (p. 45), produced the definitive edition of Scott's *Journal*.

Many Fellows on the literary side have added greatly to that camaraderie which should be an ingredient of the Society's meetings. One thinks, for example, of John Stuart Blackie (1809–95), Professor of Greek in Edinburgh University, of whom it was said 'there was no winter in his year, nor sorrow in his heart'. His gaiety and zest were proverbial and are illustrated by the couplet he coined epitomising the advantages of a University Chair:

> A thousand a year in my pocket
> And six months to do as I please

£1,000 in these days was a handsome sum of money, though scarcely comparable to the £2,200 Hope is said to have earned as Professor of Chemistry and Medicine at the beginning of the century. Many other Fellows have enlivened the Society's meetings among whom may be mentioned such genial characters as Lord Neaves, Sidney Newman, Melville Clark and Stanley Cursiter (*vide infra*).

The legal profession was strongly represented in the original Fellowship, a fact not surprising in view of the prominent role played by the Faculty of Advocates in instituting the Society. This is strikingly instanced by the presence at the founding meeting of 23 June 1783 of the Lord Justice Clerk, the Solicitor-General and several members of the Faculty of Advocates. In the course of time the number of Advocates in the Fellowship has fallen, but Advocates have continued and continue to make great contributions to the well-being of the Society. Notable examples are Lord Neaves (1800–76), ever welcome because of his 'intellectual sociability', who contributed both prose and verse to our *Proceedings* and *Blackwood's Magazine*. Legal luminaries who have sat in the Presidential Chair include Walter Scott, Lord Moncreiff (1879–84), and more recently Lord Cameron (1973–76), who has played an important role in reviving the Literary Class. Nor should it be forgotten that it was the Lord-Justice Clerk, the Hon. Thomas Miller of Barskimming, later Lord Glenlee, who chaired the first meeting of the Society.

Although religion is not discussed at the Society's meetings (p. 127) prominent churchmen have always featured in the Fellowship. One of the petitioners for a Royal Charter was Hugh

Blair (1718–1800), who successively held charges at Lady Yester's Church, the Canongate and St Giles. Dean Ramsay (1793–1872) was an enthusiastic Fellow who took a broad view of the function of the Society and stated his opinion that 'The Royal Society [of Edinburgh] should draw round it men of all pursuits' (p. 14). In this he was reiterating the views of Bishop Terrot, a distinguished churchman and mathematician (p. 8). The most famous of all was Thomas Chalmers who, however, does not seem to have taken a prominent part in the Society's affairs. At the present time the Fellowship includes the Very Rev. Dr Ronald Selby Wright (F.R.S.E., 1973) and Professor John McIntyre (F.R.S.E., 1977), Dean of the Thistle, past and present Moderators of the General Assembly of the Church of Scotland respectively.

Many musicians and artists have been elected to the Fellowship. In 1785 the Rev. Walter Young (1745–1814), minister of Erskine, was elected. He was described as 'the most splendid private musician of his day' and was an accomplished pianist, violinist, and flautist. More recently two outstanding musicians have been Fellows. Donald Frances Tovey (1876–1940), internationally famous as a musicologist and concert pianist, was said by Joachim 'to be the most learned musician in Europe'. A similar judgment was given by Pablo Casals (*Sorrows and Joys*, 1970, p. 215). He was followed in the Chair of Music by Sidney Newman (1906–71), who played an important part in restoring St Cecilia's Hall as a concert centre and museum of musical instruments. More recent elections to Fellowship include Thea Musgrave (F.R.S.E., 1979), Cedric Thorpe Davie (F.R.S.E., 1978), and the conductor of the Scottish National Orchestra, Sir Alexander Gibson (F.R.S.E., 1978).

Distinguished artists who have signed the Society's Roll Book include the sculptor Sir Francis Chantrey (1781–1842) and the painters the Rev. John Thomson of Duddingston (1778–1840), Sir Henry Raeburn (1756–1823) and Sir George Harvey (1806–76), none of whom, however, took a very active part in the Society's affairs. This does not apply to Stanley Cursiter (1887–1976), a welcome and regular attender at the Society's gatherings, whose mere presence was sufficient to bring warmth and freshness to a meeting. His lectures such as that on 'A Scientific Approach to Impressionism' were invariably a delight. To this distinguished band must be added the names of two Presidents of the Royal

Scottish Academy: Sir William MacTaggart (1903–81) and Sir Robin Philipson (F.R.S.E., 1977), who not only gave a very interesting lecture to the Society on 'A Personal Response to Colour and Light in Painting', but also gifted one of his paintings that he used to illustrate part of his lecture.

Other Branches of Science, Erudition and Taste

It will have been observed that two subjects, religion and politics, have been studiously omitted from the Society's discussions. Such omissions can perhaps be traced back to proposed regulations (1737) of the Edinburgh Society for Improving Arts and Sciences which stated that: 'In the Meetings of the Society no conversations are to be allowed in Religious or Political Disputes'.[39] On the wisdom of this dictum the Society never seems to have had any doubts, particularly on religious topics. Bishop Terrot strongly recommended the avoidance of 'unholy contests of intolerant religionists' and Lord Neaves advocated 'abstinence from such [religious] controversies'. On the other hand as stressed by Edward Sang the Society accepts that in some discussions on historical or literary subjects reference to religious opinion may well be necessary for an adequate treatment of the subject.[40] Similar strictures apply to politics. In short it seems to be generally accepted that omission of religion and politics from the Society's forum is expedient. It is therefore not surprising that except for one or two papers such as Thomas A. Wise's 'Buddhist Opinions and Monuments of Asia' (*Trans.*, 1855, 21, 255) and 'Some Indian Idols' by W. A. Cadell (*ibid.*, 1823, 9, 381) few papers on religion or politics are to be found in the Society's publications.

These two papers might be regarded as belonging more fittingly to archaeology, a science which has only spasmodically attracted the attention of the Society. On other pages the researches of Piazzi Smyth on the Great Pyramid (p. 74) and of J. Y. Simpson (p. 70) are mentioned. For the next hundred years except for one or two papers such as that of the eminent amateur Robert Munro (1835–1920) on 'A Sketch of Lake Dwelling Research' (*Proc.*, 1892–95, 20, 385) the Society's publications contain little of archaeological significance, but in recent years lectures such as Dr K. A. Steer's (F.R.S.E., 1970) 'Archaeology and Petrology in Scotland' and Dr Alexander Thom's more speculative 'Astronomy of Megalithic Man' attracted good audiences who found both lectures absorbingly interesting.[41]

It is the proud boast of the Society that Adam Smith was a founder member, but he made no contribution to the Society's activities other than by acting as first President of the Literary Class. Another founder member was James Anderson (1736–1808), an economist who is credited with identifying the core of the economic theory of rent, which is usually associated with the name of David Ricardo. Skipping the years and coming to the present century we find in the Fellowship Joseph Shield Nicholson (1850–1927) and Sir Alexander Gray (1882–1968), distinguished economists who, however, never introduced their science into the Society's discussions or publications. It would seem that the Society does not furnish a congenial outlet for the dismal science. An exception to this was the large and interested audience which attended Professor T. L. Johnston's (F.R.S.E., 1979) lecture on Adam Smith in 1977 (p. 28).

Occasionally Fellows have deserted their chosen careers to enter the economics field. Walter Scott wrote his famous *Letters of Malachi Malagrowther*, which dealt with the currency of the three kingdoms, and displayed a thorough knowledge of the fundamental principles of Scottish banking. Thomas Chalmers, Professor of Divinity in Edinburgh University, wrote a book on *Political Economy* 'as by an ecclesiastic who values economy'. Still less expected is a paper by Mossman on the 'Meteorology of Edinburgh' (*Trans.*, 1900–04, **40**, 469) which contains a discussion on the relationship between the price of first quality wheat and the weather (1801–1900).

Geography with its many branches is perhaps not easy to define especially with its frequent overlaps into meteorology, cartography, exploration, etc. Indeed it was slow to be recognised as a separate science and it was not until 1908 that Edinburgh University was the first in Scotland to establish a lectureship in geography. It is therefore not surprising that geographical topics have appeared only occasionally in the Society's publications. None the less one of the founders of modern geography was Hugh R. Mill (1861–1950), who was a Fellow of the Society for 65 years and made important investigations on rainfall and the physical geography of the Clyde Sea area (*Trans.*, 1894–96, **38**, 1).

About the same time Sir John Murray carried out his comprehensive bathymetrical surveys of the Scottish fresh-water lochs. Earlier geographical contributions include letters to Joseph Black from John Thomas Stanley on Hot Springs in Iceland (*Trans.*, 1789–93, **3**, 127, 138) and the Depletion or Drying-up of the Rivers Teviot, Nith and Clyde by David Milne (*ibid.*, 1836–40, **14**, 449). Water in one form or another has evidently attracted the notice of Scottish geographers and this tradition was maintained in 1978 when Professor J. T. Coppock (F.R.S.E., 1976) lectured to the Society on 'Resource Management in Scotland: the Case of Water'.

It is not generally recognised that David Livingstone's great African expeditions were made possible by the generosity of James Young. Livingstone and Young formed a life-long friendship when they were students at Anderson's College and Young contributed generously to Livingstone's second, third and final expeditions and any monetary promise given by Livingstone to a Portuguese trader or Arab slave dealer, even on an old bit of leather or piece of bark, was duly honoured by Young.

The scope of the Society's lectures and publications has not unnaturally been affected by the institution of other societies, and it is perhaps regrettable that matters geographical, for example, feature less than might be expected in the Society's programme. We may rest assured, however, that they are in the good hands of the Royal Scottish Geographical Society, founded at the suggestion of James Geikie, with John G. Bartholomew as its first Honorary Secretary. The R.S.E. has always welcomed the formation of other learned societies and has willingly lent a helping hand when asked. True, relations between the Society and the Society of Antiquaries of Scotland were for many years strained (p. 3), but as recorded elsewhere Fellows of the R.S.E. played an important role in its revival after years of decline. It may be said in fact that the only society to be formed without the complete approbation of the Society was the Wernerian Natural History Society (1808–38), which was formed by Robert Jameson in direct opposition to the R.S.E. Even this event did not upset the Society unduly and Brewster quietly commented that 'what was a loss to us was a gain to science' (*Proc.*, 1866, **5**, 321).

Historical topics in the Society's addresses and publications are notable by their infrequency and those which were published in the early days did not always attract favourable notice. Alexander Fraser Tytler's 'Remarks on a Mixed Species of Evidence in Matters of History' (*Trans.*, 1805, **5**, 119), for example, was criticised by the *Edinburgh Review* (1803, **1**, 505) as a paper on 'one of the least interesting subjects upon which a learned society could possibly bestow its Attention'. In more recent times historical lectures have tended to be on the scientific side and are exemplified by the Alembic Club lectures (p. 148) and Professor H. Butterfield's James Scott Prize Lecture in 1961 on 'The Place of the Scientific Revolution in the History of Thought'. With the recent rebirth of the Literary Class history may expect to gain its rightful place in the Society's syllabus. An excellent start was made in 1979 when Professor Gordon Donaldson (F.R.S.E., 1978) gave an informative lecture on 'The origins and early development of the learned professions in Scotland'.

Valuable contributions to the history of the Society are to be found in books and articles written by Fellows (see Bibliography, p. 157) including J. D. Forbes, J. Kendall, Cargill Knott, Douglas Guthrie and in a Thesis by S. A. Shapin, while scattered throughout *Proceedings* and the *Year Book* much of historical interest is to be found.

Notes

1 A reason for Blair's appointment is given by Grant: 'This Professorship was probably instituted at the suggestion of the Town Council, its object being, perhaps, to provide for the instruction of mates and skippers of the merchant service shipping from the Port of Leith'.

2 Curiously enough John Allan Broun was not a Fellow of the Society although three volumes of *Transactions* were devoted to his researches. He was closely associated with Sir Thomas Makdougall Brisbane.

3 The incident was described by Hutton Balfour in the *Edin. Phil. J.*, 1848, **45**, 122. See also F. Bell, *Proc. Cotteswold Nat. Fld Club*, 1972, **36**, 70. Sir Douglas MacLagan wrote a song entitled 'The Battle of Glen Tilt' which contains the following verse:

> The Duke cam' o'er, wi' gillies four,
> To mak' a stour and drive Balfour
> Frae 'yont the Hielan' hills, man
> 'Twas trespass clear their comin' here,
> For they wad fear awa' his deer,
> Among the Hielan' hills, man.

4 'There is perhaps no other instance of a graduation thesis so weighted with significant novelty' (Dictionary of National Biography).

5   Mary E. Weeks, *J. Chem. Educ.*, 1954, **11**, 101.
6   Demitrius Ivanovitch Mendelejeff (1834–1907; Hon. F.R.S.E., 1888).
7   Newlands' failure to convince his colleagues was at least partly due to the faulty atomic weights he employed.
8   In 1821 Leonard Horner (1785–1864) founded the Edinburgh School of Arts and Mechanics Institute, which in 1851 became the Watt Institution and School of Arts. In 1885 the Institution's endowments were amalgamated with those of George Heriot's Hospital. The Heriot–Watt College as it was then called achieved university status when Her Majesty the Queen in 1966 approved the Charter establishing the Heriot–Watt University.
9   See also *John Scott Russell* by George S. Emmerson (John Murray, 1977).
10   The statement in the text about patents is not quite correct. Charles A, Stevenson in 1892 took out a patent, not to make money by Royalties, but simply to secure his claim as inventor of the Leader System.
11   David Stevenson also reported earthquakes noted by lighthouse keepers in various parts of Scotland (*Proc.*, 1876–77, **9**, 403).
12   The story of the Stevenson family was later written by Craig Mair under the title *A Star for Seamen* (John Murray, 1980).
13   See also D. R. Dean, James Hutton and his Public, 1785–1802, *Ann. Sci.*, 1973, **30**, 89; Derek Flinn, James Hutton and Robert Jameson, *Scot. J. Geol.*, 1980, **16**, 251; Jessie M. Sweet and C. D. Waterston, Robert Jameson's Approach to the Wernerian Theory of the Earth, *Ann. Sci.*, 1967, **23**, 81.
14   It must be pointed out, however, that Hutton's paper is remarkably free from jargon. As Christison said: 'In his [Hutton's] essay of 96 quarto pages he has given his successors in all branches of science a remarkable lesson—a most luminous narrative on a most novel subject, without coining a single new term, or quitting plain English words'.
15   A facsimile of *Illustrations of the Huttonian Theory of the Earth* with an introduction by George W. White was published by the University of Illinois, Urbana, 1956.
16   *Proc.*, 1862–66, **5**, 322.
17   Dr A. Mackie (F.R.S.E., 1938) succinctly outlines the controversy thus: 'Werner and the Neptunians believed that all rocks were formed by aqueous precipitation, whereas Hutton and the Vulcanists maintained that rocks such as granites and basalts were formed by the solidification of igneous melts' (*Chem. and Ind.*, 1976, 101).
18   Jameson's distinguished pupils included J. D. Forbes, Edward Forbes, Charles Maclaren, Lord Greenock, John Goodsir, James Nicol (1810–79, Professor of Natural History at Aberdeen University), Charles Darwin and Ami Boué (President of the Geological Society of France).
19   M. J. S. Rudwick, *Brit. J. Hist. Sci.*, 1962–63, **1**, 117.
20   That the Parallel Roads still interest geologists is shown by a paper by J. B. Sissons (*Boreas*, 1978, **7**, 229).
21   Jules Henri Poincaré (1854–1912).
22   George Boole's name is associated with the algebra of Logic which has been extensively applied to the development of digital communication.

According to Bertrand Russell: 'Pure mathematics was discovered by George Boole in a work which he called the Laws of Thought'. Professor G. R. Nicoll (F.R.S.E., 1976) has pointed out that the Society appreciated the importance of Boole's work by awarding him the Keith Prize for his memoir in *Transactions*, 1857, **21**, 597, entitled 'On the Application of the Theory of Probabilities to the Question of the Combination of Testimonies or Judgments'.

23 Hughes Bennett detested the term 'physiology' and much preferred the older title 'Institutes of Medicine'.

24 E. Duvall and A. Currie, *The First Hundred Years of the Department of Pathology in Edinburgh University (1831–1931)*.

25 Such was the demand for off-prints of Aitken's papers that some were reprinted and issued as one pamphlet.

26 It should be added that earlier Walter Scott and Leonard Horner were both intimately involved in the founding of Edinburgh Academy. Another famous school, the Royal High School of Edinburgh, also produced many distinguished Fellows including Dugald Stewart, Walter Scott, Leonard Horner, James Syme, Sir John Robison, Thomas Allan, George Wilson and Lord Neaves.

27 The collection contains specimens gathered by W. S. Bruce in the *Scotia* and the Shackleton Antarctic Expeditions and by Sir John Murray in the West of Scotland.

28 The Rev. William Whewell (1794–1866; Hon. F.R.S.E., 1845), a Cambridge mathematician and philosopher of science, invented the word *science* in 1834 and reasserted its usefulness in 1840. It was little used until the end of the nineteenth century and as late as 1924 was the subject of an instruction from Council to the General Secretary that the Society had no occasion to use the word and 'while it did not expressly banish it, the opinion was generally expressed by the Council that as individuals they would prefer that its use should not be encouraged. They would be sorry to see it admitted to the pages of *Nature*'. D'Arcy Thompson thought that 'the word has been in low company and I should be very slow to introduce it into better' (*Nature, Lond.*, 1924, **114**, 824).

29 *James Clerk Maxwell* by Ivan Tolstoy (Canongate, 1981).

30 In another place Tait stated that Clerk Maxwell's '*Electricity and Magnetism* to be one of the greatest monuments ever raised to the genius of a single individual'.

31 F. Bell, *Chem. and Ind.*, 1957, 85.

32 Was this perhaps due to the fact that Council was composed of elder statesmen? Crum Brown had ceased to carry out research, but Kelvin, then President of the Society, published some 40 papers between his retiral in 1899 and his death in 1907, several of which dealt with atomic structure and radio-activity. He was also enthusiastic over the work of Becquerel, Crookes, and the Curies, but was unsympathetic to the new revolutionary ideas of the structure of matter. It is probably fair to say (as D'Arcy Thompson said of Larmor) that Kelvin 'was open to all the new knowledge, but had little relish for the new ideas'.

It is also possible that the Society felt that the discussions in which Rutherford (1871–1937; Hon. F.R.S.E., 1921), Soddy, Kelvin, J. J. Thomson and Oliver Lodge participated were too inconclusive to merit a lecture. One thing is certain. Of the concept that Dalton's indivisible atom had been replaced by an atom with a structure of its own the Society seems not to have heard a whisper.

33 William Robertson, of course, played a key role in the foundation of the Society (p. 40), but subsequently took little part in its activities. His successors as Principal at Edinburgh University, the Rev. George Husband Baird (1761–1840) and the Rev. John Lee (1779–1859) were also Fellows, but Brewster was the first Principal to combine his academic post with active research and participation in the Society's affairs.

34 See 'The Work of David Octavius Hill' by A. Dunbar (F.R.S.E., 1943), *Photogr. J.*, 1964, **104**, 53.

35 G. Colman Green, *Nature, Lond.*, 1946, **157**, 465. D. Bolton, *Chem. and Ind.*, 1976, 701.

36 Leonard Dobbin, 'The History and Discovery of Phosgene'. *Ann. Sci.*, 1945, **5**, 270.

37 See also D. Guthrie, *Year Book*, 1958, 5.

38 Hugh Blair's lectures on *Rhetoric and Belles Lettres* continue to have relevance for both teachers and students of Rhetoric. See Mary Jane W. Scott, *Univ. Edin. J.*, 1980, **29**, 323.

39 In 1791 and 1792 the Rev. Dr Ogilvy (1733–1813) of Midmar read three papers on the Theory of Plato, but Council decided that 'the discussion of a religious nature contained in these learned communications, rendered an admission of it among their papers inconsistent with their plan'. The meaning of this descision is perhaps not quite clear and commenting on it Christison raised the question: 'what is the definition of a theological discussion' (*Proc.* 1868–69, **6**, 393, 397). Instructive is Lord Neaves' verdict that: '. . . abstinence for such [religious] controversies is recommended . . . by the interests of Religion itself, which might otherwise become the object of constant attacks which there might be no adequate opportunity to obviate or answer'. Council Minute, 17 April 1868.)

40 'There must occur cases connected with History, Antiquity, and General Literature in which a casual reference to religious opinion is essential to the treatment of the subject. In such I do not see that there can be the slightest objection'. (Sang, Council Minute, 17 April 1868.)

41 Another exception is V. G. Childe's (1892–1957) lecture on 'The Early Colonization of North-eastern Scotland' (*Proc.*, 1930, **50**, 51).

CHAPTER VII

The Years of Change

The early part of the 1960s saw the first signs of important changes in the thinking of the Fellowship as a whole and of the Council in particular. During the terms of office of Sir Edmund Hirst as President and Professor Norman Feather as General Secretary, the Council embarked on a programme of improvements to the rooms including reconstruction of the Lecture Hall and redecoration of the Reception Room—for the first time in a period of fifty years. About the same time, the Society began to take steps to hold meetings in centres outside Edinburgh and the first of these was held in Perth in February 1963.

Problems were beginning to be experienced in finding space to house the Society's library. In addition, the advent of many new specialised scientific journals, published either by societies or by commercial publishers, was beginning to have a serious impact upon the receipt of papers for publication by the Society. An indication of the more outward looking attitude of the Society was the reintroduction of Conversaziones, the first of which was held in Edinburgh in 1959. These have continued over the years since and have proved popular with Fellows and their guests.

By the middle of the decade it had become apparent that the problems of library accommodation and of declining receipts of papers for publication by the Society were very serious and the Council, with Professor Norman Feather as President and Dr Anthony Ritchie (F.R.S.E., 1951) as General Secretary, set in motion a review of the functions of the Society in the second half of the century. Simultaneously the question of the Society's House came under active consideration, the main possibilities being to find alternative accommodation in central Edinburgh or to find some means of reconstructing and reorganising the rooms at 22–24 George Street so as to provide improved library facilities, rooms for meetings and offices for the conduct of the business of the Society. Discussions with our 'landlords' of the day, the Ministry of Public Building and Works had proved very discouraging and in the short term Council took steps to deal temporarily with the problem. The Fellowship as a whole was informed of this thinking in 1967 and their individual views as to how the Society might develop in future were solicited.

Over the next few years active discussion of all these problems continued and in 1967 a memorandum was submitted to the National Libraries' Committee (chaired by Dr—later Sir Frederick —F. S. Dainton, F.R.S.) in the expectation that the report of that committee might offer some guidance as to the anticipated pattern of library development in Scotland. Regrettably this was not to be and when the Report was published it became evident that the Society would require to develop its own strategy for the future of its library.

In the same year, a television programme about the work and activities of the Society was produced by the British Broadcasting Corporation and transmitted on 5 October.

The years 1967 and 1968 saw further discussions by the Council as to the future development of the Society's activities, particularly in relation to the library, the scope of meetings, the possible renovation of the Society's rooms and the need to review policy in relation to publications. These gave rise amongst other things to a series of lectures on specialised topics to be delivered in Scottish schools with the object of attracting the interest of Scottish school children to the many changes that were occurring in the various branches of science. This series continued until 1969. In that period also Consultant Architects, Henry Wylie and Partners, were appointed to draw up proposals for the renovation of the rooms.

In 1970 Sir Maurice Yonge was elected President. Because of changes in the Society's printers no *Year Book* was issued and a combined *Year Book* for 1969–71 was issued in the following session incorporating major changes in format. The receipt of papers for publication had fallen to a dangerously low level and because of this urgent consideration was given by the Council over the period 1970–72 to future policy with regard to publications. In this period also the report of the Rothschild Committee 'Framework for Government Research and Development 1972,

Cmnd 5046' recommended that the grant-in-aid to the Society, which had previously been made by the Department of Education and Science, should in future be made through the Scottish Office in Edinburgh. This represented an important change in the relationship between the Society and Government.

Beginning in 1972, under the Presidency of Lord Cameron, increasing emphasis was placed upon the organisation of symposium-type meetings with several speakers on topics of wider scientific and general interest rather than on specialised lectures given by a single speaker. These proved popular amongst Fellows and attracted larger numbers of visitors to the Society. Another major innovation was the change in policy with respect to publication in *Proceedings A*. It was agreed that with effect from January 1974 only papers in the field of mathematics would be accepted by that journal. Additionally it was decided that *Proceedings B* should give priority to the publication of studies on the Scottish natural environment. No changes in the content or format of *Transactions* were proposed at that stage. To deal with the problem of library storage, which had by that date become acute, the Council agreed to reduce the acquisition of purchased scientific periodicals by about fifty per cent after ascertaining that all the titles that were no longer being taken by the Society were readily available in other libraries in Edinburgh and other Scottish centres.

By virtue of this it was understood that any reasonable request for a journal would be met within 48 hours. Appropriately, with a Senator of the College of Justice in Scotland as President, the opportunity was taken in the session 1972–73 to revise the Laws of the Society for the first time in 25 years and the amended Laws were adopted in July 1974.

The new policy relating to *Proceedings A* was implemented in 1974 under the guidance of the Executive Editor and Chairman of the Editorial Board, Professor W. N. Everitt (F.R.S.E., 1966), and by virtue of his efforts and those of the other members of the Editorial Board proved to be very successful. The number of papers received for *Proceedings A* rose from 23 in 1973–74 to 49 in 1974–75 to 128 in 1975–76, and a very satisfactory number of manuscripts continues to be received.

Discussion about the future of the Society's library were resumed in 1973–74 when a meeting was held with the National

Library of Scotland (N.L.S.) and officials of the Scottish Education Department (S.E.D.) concerning the possibility of establishing a Scottish Science Reference Library (S.S.R.L.) by the amalgamation of the scientific holdings of the National Library of Scotland with those of the Royal Society of Edinburgh. These preliminary discussions appeared to offer a solution to the acute and growing problems facing the Society in maintaining and accommodating an ever-increasing collection of journals. At the same time they could lead to the establishment of a complete and centralised library of scientific material administered by the National Library and available to all scientists in Scotland as well as to the Fellows of the Society. The possibility emerged that the new Scottish Science Reference Library could be housed in custom-built accommodation in Edinburgh. The outcome was an agreement between the R.S.E., the N.L.S. and the S.E.D. to continue discussions along these lines, to solicit opinion from amongst the Fellowship and the major Scottish educational and research institutions, and if these were favourable to seek Government approval for the proposal. Accordingly, soundings were made widely amongst the scientific community in Scotland.

On 17 November 1975 a meeting of the Principals of the Scottish Universities together with the Directors of Government Research Institutes in Scotland was convened to consider the matter under the joint chairmanship of Lord Cameron, President of the Society, and Mr M. F. Strachan (F.R.S.E., 1979), Chairman of the Board of Trustees of the National Library of Scotland. The meeting was enthusiastic and unanimous in endorsing the proposed merger and the Council thereafter agreed to the establishment of a Joint Working Party of the Scottish Education Department, the National Library of Scotland and the Royal Society of Edinburgh to work out detailed proposals. The working party was chaired by Dr A. E. Ritchie who, as a Trustee of the N.L.S., a member of the British Library Board and the previous General Secretary of the R.S.E., was particularly knowledgeable about all aspects of the scheme and able therefore to give much advice and guidance on its development.

In the meantime, while the revised policy for *Proceedings A* was continuing to attract satisfactory numbers of good papers, contributions to *Transactions* and *Proceedings B*, apart from proceedings of Society-sponsored symposia, continued to be very small in number and in 1976 during the period of office of Dr Robin Smith as President and Professor Martin Smellie as General Secretary a working party was established to make recommendations for the future of these two journals. The working party recommended that *Transactions* should become a journal concerned, in the main, with the earth sciences and that *Proceedings B* should be for the publication of papers in the biological sciences. In the session 1977–78 when new executive editors, Professor D. R. Bowes (F.R.S.E., 1976) for *Transactions*, and Professor W. W. Fletcher (F.R.S.E., 1967) for *Proceedings B*, were appointed, along with new editorial boards, the final recommendations affecting the pattern of publication of these two journals were implemented. The editorial board of *Transactions* wished to limit the contents to the earth sciences only and with the aim of publishing more substantial papers on the basis of quarterly publication. It was decided to complete the then current volume (70) in the existing format but, as from volume 71, to publish in the new format under the title of *Transactions of the Royal Society of Edinburgh: Earth Sciences*. The editorial board of *Proceedings B* recommended that original papers should no longer be accepted and that the journal, in its existing format, should become a vehicle for the publication of symposia and symposium material in the biological sciences sponsored by the Society. These recommendations were accepted by the Council in the session 1978–79.

The first issue of the new *Transactions* appeared in 1980 and it is pleasing to record that in its revised form the journal has proved attractive to contributors and to readers. *Proceedings B* was able to anticipate its new style with the publication in 1979 of the contributions from a Symposium on the Natural Environment of the Outer Hebrides, sponsored jointly by the Society and the Nature Conservancy Council. This was followed by the publication of papers from symposia on Skin, The Tay Estuary and Sullom Voe. Others about to be published include the Natural Environment of the Inner Hebrides, Monoclonal Antibodies and Travel and Disease.

Another important recent development was the decision by the Council in 1976 to take active steps to widen the Fellowship so as to include larger numbers of Fellows from Arts and Letters and from Technology and Industry. In March 1977 the number of places for newly elected Fellows was increased from 28 to 48 to accommodate this new policy and this number was maintained in 1978 falling in 1979 to 40, in 1980 to 35 and in 1981 to 25. Also in 1977 the Council established working parties in the fields of Arts and Letters and of Technology and Industry to advise on the integration of these developing aspects of the Society's activities. In the same year the Society, together with the Scottish Council (Development and Industry), played an active role in the establishment of the Council for Applied Science in Scotland (C.A.S.S.), an organisation aimed at the promotion and application of scientific ideas and techniques in Scottish Industry.

During this period (1976-78) the Joint S.E.D./N.L.S./R.S.E. working party continued its work on the proposed S.S.R.L. development but had not yet reached final conclusions. However, discussions between the Society and the S.E.D. had indicated that the department would be prepared to consider some financial compensation to the Society if and when the Society were to make its foreign periodical holdings available for merging with those of the N.L.S. It was evident however that some years were likely to elapse before final agreement on the establishment of the S.S.R.L. and on compensation to the Society could be reached. Because of this and the greatly increased activity in relation to meetings and publications some interim reorganisation of the Society's rooms and staff responsibilities was essential.

In the spring of 1978 Miss Sandra McDougall, B.A., who had been an Administrative Assistant in the Society was appointed Meetings' Secretary and Deputy to the Executive Secretary. Her wide-ranging responsibilities included acting as Secretary to the Meetings' Committee and all the day to day matters relating to the organisation of meetings of the Society. This single step together with the active chairmanship of the Meetings' Committee by Professor Ian Sneddon contributed greatly to the successful development of a logical programme of meetings.

At the same time, in anticipation of the new initiatives on *Transactions* and *Proceedings B*, Miss Carole Anderson, B.A., was appointed to the new position of Editorial Secretary. Her responsibilities included acting as Secretary to the various editorial boards and all the technical editing and preparation of manuscripts for publication.

These two appointments represented the first steps towards the establishment of a Meetings' Office and an Editorial Office both of which were seen to be essential stages in the expansion of the Society's role.

The working parties on Arts and Letters and on Technology and Industry were by this time actively considering the roles of Fellows in these fields in the future work of the Society and the increasing numbers of Fellows in these disciplines were beginning to make an impact on the meetings programme. C.A.S.S. under the chairmanship of Sir Michael Swann (now Lord Swann, F.R.S.E., 1953) was also active in canvassing support and information in Scottish industry and commerce.

At this stage progress on the proposed S.S.R.L. development appeared slow. The Joint Working Party of the S.E.D., the N.L.S. and the R.S.E. had reaffirmed its support for the project and had submitted an agreed Feasibility Report to the Scottish Education Department. This did not appear to have been received with great enthusiasm by the Department partly it seemed because of the very considerable financial implication. The impending Referendum on the establishment of a Scottish National Assembly also introduced a considerable degree of uncertainty into the deliberations and officials of the Scottish Office and Ministers themselves were at this time extremely reluctant to make any definite commitments to the future. Nevertheless, the Council felt it essential to make further progress on plans for redevelopment of the rooms in George Street. Sketch plans for possible developments were prepared by Messrs Robert Hurd and Partners, architects in Edinburgh, and a series of sketches were also prepared by senior students in the Department of Building in Heriot-Watt University under the direction of Professor V. B. Torrance and Mr S. J. Barron. Preliminary costings on all these schemes indicated a likely cost for the redevelopment in the region of £300,000.

The following session 1978–79 saw little evidence of progress with the redevelopment plans. Partly because by that time a General Election was pending and partly because of the rapid deterioration in the general economic climate Ministers proved very hesitant about making any decisions on the S.S.R.L. project. By this time the Society was under considerable pressure to implement new regulations on fire safety. This work had been delayed because the costs were likely to be heavy and the necessary alterations were in any case embodied in the various schemes that were under consideration for internal renovation. Since little or no progress seemed to be being made with these however it seemed as if it might become necessary to embark on alterations to satisfy the fire safety regulations. Investigations into the requirements of these however quickly ran into difficulties because 22–24 George Street is a listed building and the work demanded by the fire regulations ran wholly counter to the requirements of the local Planning Department and the Historic Building Commission. As an interim measure, until approved alterations had been completed, it became necessary to limit the numbers of visitors using the lecture room and other rooms on the upper floors.

In the session 1979–80 Sir Kenneth Blaxter was elected President in succession to Dr R. A. Smith and a number of new developments occurred. The Council in the previous year had taken a decision to initiate a series of Christmas Lectures designed to draw the attention of children in their later years of secondary school to modern developments in science. The first of these lectures 'Organic Chemistry To-day' was delivered in Strathclyde University in Glasgow in December 1980 by Professor J. I. G. Cadogan (F.R.S.E., 1964), Chief Scientist of British Petroleum Chemicals Ltd, formerly of the Department of Chemistry in Edinburgh University. This lecture was repeated in Edinburgh on the following day and was warmly appreciated by an overall total of more than 700 in the two audiences.

The position with respect to the S.S.R.L. development and the renovation of the rooms in George Street improved greatly during the winter when the report of the Joint S.E.D./N.L.S./R.S.E. working party received approval from the Secretary of State for Scotland and negotiations were able to begin as to the compensation to be received by the Society in return for the handing over to the National Library of Scotland our holdings of foreign periodicals. These negotiations reached a conclusion in the autumn of 1980 when the Secretary of State offered a capital sum of £500,000 at 1979 prices and agreed to provide an annual allocation of £60,000 at 1980 prices to fund up to six Postdoctoral Research Fellowships to be awarded by the Society and tenable in Scottish seats of learning or centres of research. These offers were accepted by the Council early in January 1981 and an announcement about the establishment of the S.S.R.L. was made in Parliament on twenty-fourth March of that year.

By the end of 1980 the revised form of *Proceedings B* (Biological Sciences) was beginning to prove attractive to the subscribers and readers and *Transactions*, in its new format, was succeeding in attracting a significant number of good papers in the Earth Sciences.

The session 1981–82 saw great activity on the part of the Council. The decision was taken that a part, about 50 per cent, of the sum provided by the Secretary of State should be used to finance the reconstruction and renovation of the rooms in George Street and that the residue should be set aside to form a fund to finance anticipated extensions of the work of the Society in future. It was decided that the reconstruction of the rooms should provide a good lecture theatre for an audience of 120–150, that the heating, electrical and plumbing services should be renewed, that a Fellows' library should be established and that suitable rooms should be constructed for use by the staff of the Society and by the various sub-committees of Council. Included in the plans was provision for new cloakrooms and kitchens and the work required to meet the fire regulations.

Detailed negotiations were carried forward with architects and the various consultants with a view to agreeing a scheme that would meet the needs of the Society for the foreseeable future while containing the costs within the limits set by Council. Inevitably perhaps, the overall costs, including fees and Value Added Tax, came to a figure higher than the Council wished to commit from the Society's own resources and the decision was taken to approach the Wolfson Foundation and certain other charitable trusts and commercial and industrial institutions with a request for financial assistance. At the time of writing the Wolfson Foundation and the Wellcome Trust have each offered grants of £50,000 for which the Council was extremely grateful.

By the end of 1981 a satisfactory redevelopment scheme was agreed at costs which the Council found acceptable and the architects were instructed to proceed.

While these discussions were in progress the Library Committee, under the chairmanship of the Curator, Mr Douglas Henderson, made a detailed survey of the library so as to decide on proposals for the future of those sections of the library not being transferred to the National Library of Scotland. These consisted of two main parts, the holdings of British periodicals and the collection of monographs, some of which were extremely valuable. On the recommendation of the Library Committee, Council agreed that, with certain exceptions which were to be retained in the Society's rooms, the holdings of British periodicals and the monographs should be sold. Satisfactory arrangements were also made to ensure good access to the new S.S.R.L. by Fellows of the Society as well as by other members of the scientific community in Scotland.

Work on the transfer of the foreign periodicals to the National Library of Scotland began in the spring of 1981 and was completed by the autumn. The British periodicals that were being disposed of were removed in the autumn and the process of selecting the monographs to be retained was put in hand. The intention was to retain monographs written by Fellows of the Society and other volumes of particular relevance to Edinburgh and to the Society.

During the year it became evident that the Society would require temporary accommodation in which to continue its work during the period of reconstruction and renovation and negotiations were conducted with the Institute of Chartered Accountants of Scotland for the lease of office accommodation at 29 Queen Street and for the use of their lecture theatres at 27 Queen Street. These reached a successful conclusion in the autumn of 1981 and from 5 January 1982 the Society was located in 29 Queen Street.

In embarking upon this major redevelopment scheme the Council was most anxious that the work should be completed by 1983 when the Society would be celebrating its bicentenary. Because of the lengthy delays in concluding negotiations with the Scottish Education Department it seemed at one stage as if this was a forlorn hope. However the architects were of the opinion that the renovation could be completed in a maximum of 15 months and as work commenced in April 1982 there is every prospect that the Society will be able to reoccupy the rooms in George Street during the latter part of the 1982–83 session, its Bicentenary year.

Also during 1981–82 planning for the Bicentennial celebrations began in earnest and a Bicentenary Committee was set up by Council under the chairmanship of The Very Reverend Professor John McIntyre. When Professor McIntyre became Moderator-Elect of the General Assembly of the Church of Scotland in 1981,

Professor George Boyd of Edinburgh University succeeded him as chairman. This committee planned a programme of special meetings integrated with the regular meetings programme of the Society, and in consultation with the Executive Editors of *Proceedings A*, *Proceedings B* and *Transactions* arranged for special publications by these journals. Additionally the Council had some time earlier commissioned Professor Neil Campbell, one of our most senior Fellows, to write an account of the Society since its foundation to be published at the time of the Bicentenary and this chapter forms a small part of that volume.

The many other new initiatives taken by the Society in recent years have continued to flourish. The second Christmas Lecture for schools was delivered in Glasgow and again in Edinburgh by Dr A. J. Hale, Vice-President, European Pre-clinical Research and Development, G. D. Searle and Co. Ltd, on 'Biotechnology: Old and New'. The publications of the Society in their new forms continued to progress as did the work of the Society in the fields of Arts and Letters and Industry and Technology. The first of the new Royal Society of Edinburgh Postdoctoral Research Fellowships was awarded in December 1981 and the collaboration between the Society and the organisers of national and international conferences in Edinburgh became a regular and recognised feature of the Society's work.

Having set in hand an ambitious programme of redevelopment of the Society's rooms and of its future scope of activity the Council was very concerned to ensure that the finances of the Society were placed on a sound foundation. To this end a substantial part of the compensation received from the Secretary of State in return for the transfer of our foreign periodicals to the National Library of Scotland was set aside as a capital fund to help finance future activities. To this will be added the proceeds of the sales of those British periodicals and monographs not being retained by the Society. The Council however was also of the opinion that the Fellows of the Society themselves would wish an opportunity to contribute personally to these new developments and accordingly launched a Bicentennial Appeal Fund to provide funds to assist in financing other activities such as, for example, the installation of equipment to facilitate the more effective use of the new rooms by Fellows, assistance with travel expenses for visits abroad or for visitors from overseas, awards to recognise new inventions or developments by scientists and technologists in Scotland and assistance with the organisation of meetings or symposia in Scotland. This fund has now accumulated donations or covenants to a total value of £30,000.

This is a particularly suitable time to review the progress of the Society. It has been done on a number of previous occasions, notably by J. D. Forbes, William Turner and D'Arcy Thompson but the changes now in hand are more momentous than any in the past except for the original foundation of the Society and its removal to George Street. Many hazards and difficulties lie ahead but given that we and our successors can show the same dedication and enthusiasm as our predecessors there is little doubt that an exciting prospect lies ahead and that the Society will serve to keep future generations of Fellows and scholars abreast of new developments and provide them with opportunities for the 'cultivation of every branch of science, erudition and taste'.

CHAPTER VIII

Miscellanea

The Royal Society of Edinburgh Club*

*Douglas Guthrie (1885–1975), *The Royal Society Club of Edinburgh*, 1962

Conviviality and learned societies are no strangers to one another and indeed the Royal Society of London was the outcome of gatherings of a few enthusiasts who banded together about 1650 in the Mitre or Bull-Head to discuss science. Such an intimate initiation cannot be claimed for our Society although as has been pointed out (p. 2) the Rankenian Club may be regarded as a fore-runner of the R.S.E. In 1820 thirty-seven years after the founding of the Society it was decided to form a club open to Fellows 'with the view of promoting the objects of the Royal Society'. Member-ship was originally restricted to forty-six, but in 1950 was increased to sixty and in 1981 to sixty-six.

The Club dines several times a year, generally in the Society's rooms with occasional outings elsewhere. Although dinner jackets are *de rigueur* the dinners are essentially informal and *gemütlich*. Guests frequently include the afternoon's lecturer and lengthy speechification is normally not regarded with pleasure or satisfaction. Originally the dinners were held before the Society's meetings.

The Club has included in its membership many distinguished Fellows including Walter Scott, third President of the Society (1820–32). Scott's *Journal* gives some idea of the Club's activities. The entry for 5 December 1825 reads: 'Dined with the Royal Society Club, where, as usual, was a pleasant meeting of from twenty to twenty-five. It is a very good institution. We pay two guineas only for six dinners in the year present or absent. Dine at five or rather ½ past five at the Royal Hotel, where we have an

146

excellent dinner, with soups, fish, etc. and all in good order. Port and sherry till half-past seven then coffee and we go to the Society. This has great influence in keeping up the attendance—it being found that this preface of a good dinner to be paid for whether or not brings out many a philosopher who might not otherwise have attended the Society'. A much less cheerful note is sounded in the entry for 17 January 1826 when Scott was unhappy and uncertain with bankruptcy hanging over him: '. . . have apologised [for not] attending the Royal Society Club . . .' (p. 124).

The Club seems to have flourished from the start and that the jovial spirit of its gatherings has prevailed may be gleaned from Archibald Geikie's *Scottish Reminiscences* (1905): 'The most noted survivor of these old social gatherings in Edinburgh is the "Royal Society Club". This association was founded to promote good fellowship among the Fellows of the Royal Society [of Edinburgh] and to ensure a nucleus for the evening meetings. The Club has from the beginning been limited in numbers, but has always included the most distinguished and "clubable" of the Fellows. It meets in some hotel on the evenings on which the Society's meetings are held, and after a pleasant dinner, with talk and songs, its members adjourn in time to take their places in the Society's hall. When Neaves, Maclagan, Blackie, Christison, and Macnee were present, it will be understood how joyous such gatherings were. Many a good song was written for these occasions, and many a good story was told. A favourite ditty by Maclagan, sung by him with much effect, ended with the following verse, which illustrates the delightful mixture of science and fun with which the professor was wont to regale us.

> Lyon Playfair last winter took up a whole hour
> To prove so much mutton is just so much power;
> He might have done all that he did twice as well
> By an hour of good feeding at Slaney's Hotel;
> And instead of the tables he hung on the wall,
> Have referred to the table in this festive hall;
> And as for his facts—have more clearly got at 'em
> From us than from Sappers and Miners at Chatham.

>> Whilst like jolly good souls,
>> We emptied our bowls,
>> And so washed down our grub

147

In a style worth the name,
Wealth, honour, and fame
Of the Royal Society Club.'

Gradually, but regrettably, home-made songs gave way to story and anecdote and efforts to revive the Victorian atmosphere of the smoking concert were unsuccessful, so much so that one member, W. B. Blaikie (1847–1927), the author of the Club song, in October 1925 'praised the uproarious days of old as compared with the Sunday School behaviour of the present company'! Blaikie, it may be interpolated, was a delightful character who succeeded in maintaining a friendship with such diverse characters as Robert Louis Stevenson and W. E. Henley. Harmony still reigns at the dinners though not in the musical sense and members enjoy the pleasures of a good dinner, congenial company and warm friendship.

The Alembic Club

The following account of the Alembic Club is based on articles by James Kendall in *Nature, London*, 1952, **170**, 959 and *Endeavour*, 1954, **13**, 94.

On 29 October 1889, the five non-professorial members of the teaching staff of the Chemistry Department of the University of Edinburgh formed themselves into 'The Alembic Club' with the the aim of bringing historical matter connected with chemistry within the reach of interested readers. The original members were John Gibson (1855–1914), well known as one of the authors of the Crum-Brown-Gibson rule of benzene substitution, and later Professor of Chemistry at the Heriot-Watt College; Leonard Dobbin, who acted as Secretary of the Club until 1946; Hugh Marshall (1868–1913), later Professor of Chemistry in University College, Dundee; James Walker (p. 80), and Alexander Smith (1865–1922), later President of the American Chemical Society in 1911.

The Club prospered, largely due to the efforts of Leonard Dobbin (1858–1952), whose 71 years of Fellowship (1881–1952) equal the record held by the civil engineer and geologist Sir Richard Griffith, Bart (1784–1878), 'the Father of Irish Geology'. In 1946 Dobbin handed over his office to James Kendall, who suggested a few years later that a committee should be set up to make recommendations for the administration of the Club on a broader and firmer basis under the *aegis* of the Royal Society of Edinburgh. The Committee duly met and its recommendations were accepted by Council and by the Alembic Club in 1952. As a result the Alembic Club now consists of five members with a special interest in the history of science together with the President, General Secretary, Treasurer and Curator of the Society. The Secretary is the General Secretary of the Society assisted by a member as Assistant Secretary. The Club is a self-perpetuating body whose aim is to publish reprints of classic papers in chemistry and adjoining fields of science; arrange lectures to be delivered at unspecified intervals; and award the Alembic Club Prize of £50 quinquennially to a distinguished historian of science, provided funds are available for this purpose.

The main activity of the Club has been the publication of some of the less accessible chemical classics in convenient form as simple reprints (if in English) or as translations (if in a foreign language) and to date some 50,000 Reprints have been sold. It was fitting that the first *Alembic Club Reprint* should be Joseph Black's famous 'Experiments on Magnesia Alba, Quicklime, and some other Alkaline Substances'. A list of Alembic Club Reprint titles is given on p. 150.

The Alembic Club's activities in recent years, it must be admitted, have been very limited, but the Club is now functioning with renewed zeal. The last *Reprint*, No. 22 (1958), was edited by Professor Norman Feather and contains Röntgen's fundamental papers on X-rays and one by J. J. Thomson and E. Rutherford on the same subject with an authoritative and searching historical introduction by Professor Feather.

Four Alembic Club Lectures have so far been delivered before the Society:

1. 1955 'Michael Faraday' by James Kendall
2. 1961 'Joseph Black' by Douglas McKie
3. 1969 'Scottish Chemistry in the 18th Century' by Dr Andrew Kent (1898–1976)
4. 1977 'William Cullen and the Edinburgh School of Chemistry' by A. Mackie, *Year Book*, 1978, 13.

The present membership of the Alembic Club is:
Ex officiie Members: Sir Kenneth Blaxter (F.R.S.E., 1965), R. M.

S. Smellie (F.R.S.E., 1964; Secretary), Sir John Atwell (F.R.S.E., 1963) and D. M. Henderson (F.R.S.E., 1966).
Members: R. Schlapp (F.R.S.E., 1927) and Neil Campbell (F.R.S.E., 1950; Assistant Secretary).

Alembic Club Reprints

1. Experiments upon Magnesia Alba, Quicklime, and some other Alkaline Substances by Joseph Black, M.D., 1755.
2. Foundations of the Atomic Theory. Comprising Papers and Extracts by John Dalton, William Hyde Wollaston, M.D. and Thomas Thomson, M.D., 1802–08.
3. Experiments on Air. Papers published in the *Philosophical Transactions* by the Hon. Henry Cavendish, F.R.S., 1784–85.
4. Foundations of the Molecular Theory. Comprising Papers and Extracts by John Dalton, Joseph Louis Gay-Lussac and Amedeo Avagadro, 1808–11.
5. Extracts from Micrographia by R. Hooke, F.R.S., 1665.
6. The Decomposition of the Alkalies and Alkaline Earths. Papers published in the *Philosophical Transactions* by Humphry Davy, Sec. R.S., 1807–08.
7. The Discovery of Oxygen. Part 1. Experiments by Joseph Priestley, LL.D., 1775.
8. The Discovery of Oxygen. Part 2. Experiments by Carl Wilhelm Scheele, 1777.
9. The Elementary Nature of Chlorine. Papers published in the *Philosophical Transactions* by Humphry Davy, Sec. R.S., 1810–18.
10. Researches on the Arseniates, Phosphates, and Modifications of Phosphoric Acid by Thomas Graham, 1833.
11. Essays of Jean Rey, Doctor of Medicine. On an Enquiry into the Cause wherefore Tin and Lead increase in Weight on Calcination, 1630.
12. The Liquefaction of Gases. Papers by Michael Faraday, F.R.S., 1823–45.
13. The Early History of Chlorine. Papers by Carl Wilhelm Scheele, 1774; C. L. Berthollet, 1785; Guyton de Morveau, 1787; Joseph Louis Guy-Lussac and L. J. Thenard, 1809.
14. Researches on the Molecular Asymmetry of Natural Organic Compounds. Lectures by Louis Pasteur, 1860.

15. The Electrolysis of Organic Compounds. Papers by Hermann Kolbe, 1845–68.
16. Papers on Esterification, and the Constitution of Salts by Alexander W. Williamson, LL.D., F.R.S., 1850–56.
17. Medico-Physical Works. Being a Translation of *Tractatus Quinque Medico-physici* by John Mayow, LL.D., 1674.
18. Sketch of a Course of Chemical Philosophy by Stanislao Cannizzaro, 1858.
19. The Foundations of the Theory of Dilute Solutions. Papers on Osmotic Pressure by J. H. van't Hoff, and on Electrolytic Dissociation by Svante Arrhenius, 1887.
20. Prout's Hypothesis. Papers by William Prout, M.D., J. S. Stas and C. Marignac, 1815–60, with Introduction by Leonard Dobbin and James Kendall.
21. On a New Chemical Theory and Researches on Salicylic Acid by A. S. Couper, 1858.
22. X-Rays and the Electric Conductivity of Gases. Comprising papers by W. C. Röntgen, J. J. Thomson and E. Rutherford, 1895–96, with a historical introduction by N. Feather.

Prizes

One way in which a learned society can encourage research and scholarship is to award prizes for outstanding contributions to knowledge, particularly though not exclusively to Fellows, and the Society has at its disposal a number of prizes. These are awarded as the result of much careful consideration and deliberation as instanced by Hope when making the presentation to James D. Forbes of the Keith Prize in 1835. Having stated that 'in the ordinary case of the publication of papers, the Society holds itself in no degree responsible for the truth of the facts stated therein: but in the adjudication of prizes, the case is different: and that in regard to them the Council are bound to be satisfied of the truth of the statements for which they award their prize'. Hope goes on to inform the Society that he and some of his colleagues had made it their business to see and satisfy themselves of the accuracy of Forbes's leading experiments. Such meticulous vetting is perhaps not general practice, but Hope's strictures still hold. The honour of the Prize was heightened by Forbes' students when they presented him with a paper signed with all their names and conveying their congratulations.

The award of the Society's prizes has always been greatly valued by the recipients and is instanced by George J. Allman (1812–98), Professor of Natural History at Edinburgh University, who regarded the award to him of the Makdougall Brisbane Prize 'as one of the most cherished incidents in my life' and felt elated to be 'recognised by a body with which some of the happiest years of my life have been associated'.

The original terms of the awards are so far as possible scrupulously observed, but occasionally changing circumstances require modification of these terms. Gold medals, for example, are no longer awarded, initially because at one period (1918) gold was not available and later because it became too expensive. All but one of the Prize Medals are manufactured by Alex Kirkwood & Son, Edinburgh, who have been medallists to the Society since 1836 when the first Keith medal was struck.

The lists of recipients of the Prizes over the years makes impressive reading and contain names such as Kelvin, Clerk Maxwell, Brewster and Appleton. Details are given in the Society's *Year Book* and other publications.

In the sequel a brief account is given of the Society's prizes.

Gunning Victoria Jubilee Prize

The Prize was founded in 1887 by His Excellency, Dr R. H. Gunning (1818–1900), who spent much of his life in Brazil and was noted for his generosity. The Prize is awarded quadrennially in recognition of original work in Physics, Chemistry, or Pure or Applied Mathematics. The Prize consists of a sum of money, and is open to scientists resident in or connected with Scotland.

Neill Prize

In November 1851 the Council was informed that by the will of Patrick Neill (p. 60) the sum of £500 was bequeathed to the Society for the purpose of 'the interest thereof being applied in furnishing a medal or other award every second or third year to any distinguished Scottish Naturalist, according as such Medal or Award shall be voted by the Council of the said Society'. The Prize consists of a Medal.

Keith Prize

This Prize was gifted by Alexander Keith of Dunottar (died 1819), the first Treasurer of the Society, 'for the most important discoveries in Science made in any part of the world, but communicated by their author to the Royal Society of Edinburgh and published for the first time in the *Transactions*'. The Prize is awarded biennially in the physical and biological sciences alternately and consists of a Medal, which until *c.* 1930 was made of solid gold. James D. Forbes was Keith Prizeman three times (1833–35, 1841–43, and 1863–65), a record unlikely to be equalled, while Brewster and Tait were each awarded the Prize on two occasions.

Makdougall Brisbane Prize

In May 1855 Sir Thomas Makdougall Brisbane, Bart (p. 42) announced his intention of founding a Prize in the following terms: 'Feeling as I do a great debt of gratitude to the Royal Society of Edinburgh for the honour conferred upon me and electing me as their President, and for the kindness evinced towards me during my twenty-eight years of office I have held that distinguished office I am desirous to mark my sense of the obligations thus laid upon me in such a manner as to connect my name with the Society in an object tending to the promotion and advancement of science'. Sir Thomas laid down no rules of adjudication, but made some suggestions and the Prize in line with these suggestions is awarded biennially by the Council 'to such persons as shall appear to them most conducive to the promotion of the interests of science'. The Prize consists of a Medal (for many years made of gold).

Bruce-Preller Lecture Fund

Dr Charles S. Du Riche Preller (1844–1929), an enthusiastic Fellow, electrical engineer and amateur geologist, bequeathed in 1929 a sum of money to the Society, the income of which is applied biennially to an honorarium for a special Bruce-Preller Lecture by an outstanding scientist. The subject is described in the most general terms: 'Geology or Electrical or Physical Science, or in the discretion of the Council some other branch of Science'.

The fund was named after the donor and his wife whose maiden name was Rachel Bruce.

Bruce Prize

The Prize, founded to commemorate the work of Dr W. S. Bruce (p. 115), is awarded biennially by a Committee appointed jointly by the Royal Society of Edinburgh, the Royal Physical Society of Edinburgh and the Royal Scottish Geographical Society. The award of a Medal is made for notable contributions to Natural Sciences; the contributions to be in the nature of new knowledge, the outcome of a personal visit to polar regions by the recipient.

James Scott Prize

The Prize was funded from the estate of James Scott, a farmer at East Pittendreich, near Brechin, who died in 1896. It was founded by the Trustees of Mr Scott's Bequest in 1918, and is awarded triennially or at such intervals as Council may decide 'for a lecture or essay on the fundamental concepts of Natural Philosophy'.

David Anderson-Berry Fund

This prize of a Medal was founded by Dr David Anderson-Berry (1862–1926) who studied at the Universities of Edinburgh, Glasgow and Heidelberg. It is awarded triennially by Council for recent work on the effects of X-rays and other forms of radiation on living tissues.

Robert Cormack Bequest Fund

See p. 75.

Finance

The Royal Societies of London and Edinburgh differ from the Académie des Sciences in France in that although they enjoy the patronage of the Monarch they are in no sense Government institutions (p. 1). Without any Government advice or interference they formulate their own laws, elect governing bodies and conduct their own affairs. The Government, however, provides the accommodation which houses the Societies and makes substantial grants to aid them in their work.

In the early days the Society was entirely dependent on the subscriptions of Fellows to meet its expenditure. The entrance fee and annual subscription initially were two guineas and one guinea respectively, but over the years these have undergone considerable increases. At the present time the entrance fee is twenty pounds and the annual subscription is twenty-five pounds.

Some time after the institution of the Society the Government decided to make an annual grant of £200 to the Society and in 1836 this was raised to £300. Rather surprisingly fifty years later the Secretary to the Treasury wrote to the Society, and, referring to the grant, stated that 'there is nothing whatever to show the ground of the grant or the mode of its application'. It was left to the General Secretary of the Society to reply that the Government instead of giving the Society appartments rent free gave a grant to cover rent and taxes.

As pointed out above the Government now provides the Society with a suitable building rent free (p. 48) and makes a substantial annual grant. In addition the Society is helped by donations and legacies, and in particular is greatly indebted to the Carnegie Trust for the Universities of Scotland with which it has long and common interests. Since the foundation of the Trust in 1901 many men and women who became Fellows have been helped at various stages in their careers—student, post-graduate and staff—by assistance from the Trust in the payment of fees and subsequent research support. In 1947 the Trust decided to make an annual grant to the Society to help with the cost of its publications, and this invaluable direct form of aid has continued until the present time. The Society and the Trust have sometimes shared office-bearers and John R. Peddie (1887–1979), a former Secretary of the Trust, served on Council (1956–70). Later from 1973–76 the President, Lord Cameron, and the General Secretary, Dr Anthony Ritchie, were respectively Chairman and Secretary of the Trust.

As detailed earlier (p. 144), Council has given careful consideration in recent years to the Society's finances and steps have been taken to place them on a more secure foundation.

Museum

By its Charter the Society undertook to place any antiquarian donations in the Library of the Faculty of Advocates and any scientific donations in the Museum of the University of Edinburgh. The clear intention of the Society not to manage a museum of its own, however, underwent a change in 1797 when Hutton died and left a valuable collection of geological specimens, which on the advice of Joseph Black was given to the Society. The Society consequently found itself unable to retain a collection it greatly coveted, and after considerable discussion the collection was removed to the University. Unfortunately Jameson, an enthusiastic Wernerian (p. 87), shortly afterwards was appointed to the Chair of Natural Philosophy in the University and took no interest in the Huttonian collection which remained packed in boxes and out of sight.

Reluctantly, the Society came to the conclusion that the Huttonian Collection was 'effectively lost to them' and in 1811, to avoid a similar mishap, obtained a new Royal Charter authorising it to maintain its own museum. This was followed by gifts of geological specimens from Huttonian geologists including Lord Webb Seymour, and the appointment of a Curator of the Library and Museum testified to the Society's determination to furnish a museum with the specimens suitably arranged and displayed. Information about the history of the Museum is meagre in the extreme, but it seems certain never to have prospered. Eventually it was decided that it was inexpedient to maintain the Natural History exhibits and in 1859 they were distributed to the Royal Botanic Garden, the National Museum of Science and Industry (now the Royal Scottish Museum) and the Museums of the Royal College of Surgeons and of the Society of Advocates.

The removal of the natural history specimens may have helped accommodation problems, but it seems to have done little to make the Museum viable for in 1877 Archibald Geikie, having been requested to examine the remaining geological exhibits, stated that the Museum was 'in the highest degree unsatisfactory', having received 'no attention for many years'. It was accordingly decided to reduce the collection still further and retain only these specimens referred to in papers read before the Society and published in *Transactions* or contemporary journals or those having historical interest. In the event the Agassiz Collection was given to the Royal Scottish Museum and the remainder went to the University Department of Geology and Mineralogy. Finally, in 1910, the remaining geological and mineral specimens were distributed among these and other Scottish institutions, while the Ure, Webb Seymour and Mackenzie collections were given to Glasgow University.

The failure of the Society to maintain a well run museum was due partly to the usual problems of accommodation and funding, but mainly to the lack of a *full-time* curator who could give the undivided care and attention necessary.

A few exhibits are all that remain on view and include the Royal Charters of 1783 and 1811, the manuscript of Clerk Maxwell's first paper (p. 108) and the report on it by the referee, James D. Forbes. Interesting too is one of the Society's seals in a tin container which used to be affixed to the certificates presented to Fellows on signing the Roll. At one time the Museum contained a relic of a gruesome accident in the shape of a piece of lead which Henry Hall, Keeper on the Eddystone Lighthouse, swallowed in a molten condition while endeavouring to extinguish the fire which consumed the lighthouse in 1758. The relic is now to be seen in the Royal Scottish Museum.

On the walls of the Society's rooms are several 'museum pieces' such as the Whitelaw clock (p. 42), Piazzi Smyth's barometer and remnants of the messages in the *Scotia*'s drift bottles (p. 115).

Bibliography

Books

Robert Chambers, *Biographical Dictionary of Eminent Scotsmen*, Edinburgh, 1830.

G. Y. Craig (Editor), *James Hutton's Theory of the Earth: The Lost Drawings*, Scottish Academic Press, 1978.

A. G. Clement and R. H. S. Robertson, *Scotland's Scientific Heritage*, Oliver and Boyd, Edinburgh and London, 1961.

Alexander Grant, *The Story of the University of Edinburgh during its First Three Hundred Years*, 2 vols, London, 1884.

Cargill G. Knott, *Life and Scientific Work of Peter Guthrie Tait*, Cambridge University Press, 1911.

Cargill C. Knott (editor), *Napier Tercentenary Memorial Volume*, 1915.

Cargill C. Knott (editor), *Edinburgh's Place in Scientific Progress*, W. and R. Chambers, 1921.

Cargill C. Knott (editor), *Collected Scientific Papers of John Aitken*, 1923.

H. R. Fletcher and W. H. Brown, *The Royal Botanic Garden, Edinburgh*, H.M.S.O., Edinburgh, 1970.

Eric Linklater (1899–1974), *The Voyage of the Challenger*, John Murray Publishers Ltd, 1972.

Hugh Robert Mill, *Life Interests of a Geographer*, Privately issued, 1945.

Ruth D'Arcy Thompson, *D'Arcy Wentworth Thompson*

Articles

J. H. Ashworth, 'Charles Darwin as a Student in Edinburgh, 1825–27', *Proc.*, 1935, **55**, 97.

E. B. Bailey *et al.*, 'James Hutton, 1726–97. Commemoration of his Death', *Proc.*, 1950, **63B**, 351.

W. N. Boog-Watson, 'Sir John Murray. A Chronic Student', *Univ. Edinb. J.*, 1967, **23**, 123.

D. Brewster, 'Presidential Address', *Proc.*, 1866, **5**, 321.

H. A. Brück, *The Royal Observatory, Edinburgh*, 1822–1972, Edinburgh University Press.

N. Campbell, 'The Royal Society of Edinburgh', *Chem. and Ind.*, 1968, 783.

R. Christison, 'Presidential Address', *Proc.*, 1868, **6**, 392.

J. N. Davidson, 'The Royal Society of Edinburgh', *J. Roy. Inst. Chem.*, 1954, **78**, 562.

V. A. Eyles, 'Sir James Hall, Bt (1761–1832)', *Endeavour*, 1961, **20**, 210.

James D. Forbes, 'Presidential Address', *Proc.*, 1866, **5**, 2. *Trans.*, General Index, 1783–1888, p. 15.

D. Guthrie, 'Medical and Literary Contributions to the *Transactions of the Royal Society of Edinburgh*', *Yearbook*, 1958, p. 5.

D. Guthrie, 'A List of Portraits of the Royal Society of Edinburgh with Biographical Notes', *Yearbook*, 1959–60, p. 5.

J. P. Kendall, 'The Royal Society of Edinburgh', *Endeavour*, 1946, **5**, 54.

M. MacGregor, 'James Hutton', *Endeavour*, 1947, **6**, 109.

A. Mackie, 'A famous foursome and its influence on science and technology', *Chem. and Ind.*, 1976, p. 98.

A. Mackie, 'William Cullen and the Edinburgh School of Chemistry', *Yearbook*, 1978, 13.

Lord Moncreiff, '100 Years History of the Royal Society of Edinburgh', *Proc.*, 1883–84, **12**, 451.

Dean Ramsay, *Proc.*, 1861, **4**, 468.

James Ritchie, 'The Edinburgh Explorers', *Univ. Edin. J.*, 1942–43, **12**, 155.

James Ritchie, 'A Double Centenary—Two Notable Naturalists, Robert Jameson and Edward Forbes', *Proc.*, 1956, **66B**, 29.

W. H. Rutherford, 'History of the Royal Society of Edinburgh'. Typescript.

Steven A. Shapin, 'The Founding of the Royal Society of Edinburgh', *Brit. J. Hist. Sci.*, 1974, **7**, 1.

Bishop Terrot, *Proc.*, 1850–51, **3**, 398.

D'Arcy W. Thompson, 'Scotland and its People', *The History of Science in Scotland*, Oliver and Boyd.

D'Arcy W. Thompson, 'Fifty Years Ago in the Royal Society of Edinburgh', *Proc.*, 1933–34, **54**, 145.

William Turner, 'The Opening of the New Home of the Society', *Transactions*, General Index, 1889–1908, p. 1.

Thesis

Steven Arthur Shapin, 'The Royal Society of Edinburgh. A Study of the Social Context of Hanoverian Science' (University of Pennsylvania, 1971).

Miscellaneous

Collected Biography of the Fellows of the Royal Society of Edinburgh, 1783–1820. Compiled by Steven Shapin.

Index of Fellows of the Royal Society of Edinburgh elected from 1783–1882. Edited and introduced by Eric G. Forbes.

Minute Books of the Royal Society of Edinburgh.

One Hundred Medical and Scientific Fellows of the Royal Society of Edinburgh, elected from 1783 to 1832. Edited by Sheila Devlin-Thorp.

Proceedings of the Royal Society of Edinburgh.

Scottish Men of Science, sponsored by Eric G. Forbes (History of Medicine and Science Unit, University of Edinburgh) includes *Robert Brown* by Gay Hatfield and *James Clerk Maxwell* by Eric G. Forbes.

A series of booklets written by W. P. Doyle under the title *Chemistry in the University of Edinburgh* includes biographies of William Cullen, Lyon Playfair, Alexander Crum Brown and James Walker.

Transactions of the Royal Society of Edinburgh, General Index to the first Thirty-four Volumes (1783–1888), Edinburgh, 1890.

Transactions of the Royal Society of Edinburgh, General Index to Volumes 35–46 (1889–1908), Edinburgh, 1910.

Appendix

The Society's Officers, 1783–1983

Presidents

1783–1812	His Grace the Duke of Buccleuch
1812–1820	Sir James Hall, Bart, F.R.S.
1820–1832	Sir Walter Scott, Bart
1832–1860	Sir Thomas Makdougall Brisbane, Bart, G.C.B., G.C.H.
1860–1864	His Grace the Duke of Argyll, K.G., K.T., D.C.L., LL.D., F.R.S.
1864–1868	Principal Sir David Brewster, K.H., LL.D., D.C.L., F.R.S.
1869–1873	Sir Robert Christison, Bart, M.D., D.C.L.
1873–1878	Sir Wm. Thomson, D.C.L., F.R.S. (Lord Kelvin)
1878–1879	Rev. Philip Kelland, M.A., F.R.S.
1879–1884	The Rt. Hon. Lord Moncreiff of Tullibole, LL.D.
1884–1885	Thomas Stevenson, M.Inst.C.E.
1886–1890	Sir Wm. Thomson, LL.D., D.C.L., F.R.S. (Lord Kelvin)
1890–1895	Sir Douglas Maclagan, M.D., LL.D.
1895–1907	The Rt. Hon. Lord Kelvin, G.C.V.O., LL.D., D.C.L., F.R.S.
1908–1913	Principal Turner, K.C.B., D.C.L., LL.D., D.Sc., F.R.S.
1913–1915	Professor James Geikie, LL.D., F.R.S.
1915–1919	Dr John Horne, F.R.S.
1919–1924	Professor F. O. Bower, F.R.S.
1924–1929	Principal Sir James Alfred Ewing, K.C.B., F.R.S.
1929–1934	Professor Sir E. A. Sharpey-Schafer, F.R.S.

1934–1939	Professor D'Arcy Wentworth Thompson, Kt, C.B., LL.B., F.R.S.
1939–1943	Professor Sir Edmund Whittaker, Kt, LL.D., F.R.S.
1943–1949	Professor Sir William Wright Smith, Kt, LL.D., F.R.S.
1949–1954	Professor James P. Kendall, D.Sc., LL.D., F.R.S.
1954–1958	Professor James Ritchie, M.A., D.Sc.
1958–1959	Professor J. Norman Davidson, C.B.E., D.Sc., F.R.S.
1959–1964	Professor Sir Edmund Hirst, C.B.E., LL.D., F.R.S.
1964–1967	Professor J. Norman Davidson, C.B.E., D.Sc., F.R.S.
1967–1970	Professor Norman Feather, Ph.D., F.R.S.
1970–1973	Sir Maurice Yonge, C.B.E., D.Sc., F.R.S.
1973–1976	The Hon. Lord Cameron, D.S.C., Q.C., D.L., LL.D.
1976–1979	Professor Robert A Smith, C.B.E., F.R.S.
1979–1982	Sir Kenneth Blaxter, D.Sc., F.R.S., F.R.S.A.
1982–	Sir John Atwell, C.B.E., M.Sc., LL.D., F. Eng.

General Secretaries

1783–1798	Professor John Robison
1798–1819	Professor John Playfair, F.R.S.
1819–1828	Sir David Brewster, F.R.S.
1828–1839	Sir John Robison
1840–1860	Professor James David Forbes, F.R.S.
1860–1879	Professor John Hutton Balfour, F.R.S.
1879–1901	Professor Peter Guthrie Tait
1901–1912	Professor G. Chrystal, F.R.S.
1912–1922	Dr Cargill C. Knott, F.R.S.
1923–1933	Professor R. A. Sampson, F.R.S.
1933–1936	Professor J. H. Ashworth, F.R.S.
1936–1946	Professor J. P. Kendall, LL.D., F.R.S.
1946–1956	Dr J. E. Richey, F.R.S.
1956–1966	Professor Norman Feather, F.R.S.
1966–1976	Professor A. E. Ritchie
1976–	Professor R. M. S. Smellie

Treasurers

1783–1798	Mr Alexander Keith
1798–1820	Mr James Bonar
1821–1833	Mr Thomas Allan
1833–1834	Mr John Gardiner
1834–1836	Mr George Forbes
1836–1839	Mr Charles Forbes
1839–1857	Mr John Russell
1857–1863	Mr James T. Gibson Craig
1863–1880	Mr David Smith
1880–1893	Mr A. Gillies Smith
1894–1906	Mr Philip R. D. Maclagan
1906–1926	Mr James Currie
1927–1937	Dr James Watt
1937–1947	Sir Ernest Wedderburn
1947–1957	Mr Andrew W. Young
1957–1967	Dr John R. Peddie
1967–1977	Lord Balerno of Currie
1977–1982	Sir John Atwell
1982–	Dr Ian Forbes

Curators of the Library and Museum

1812–1819	Mr Thomas Allan
1820–1833	Mr James Skene
1834–1854	Dr Thos. S. Traill
1856–1878	Dr (Sir) Douglas Maclagan
1878–1906	Dr Alexander Buchan
1906–1916	Dr J. Sutherland Black
1916–1926	Dr A. Crichton Mitchell
1926–1939	Professor (Sir) D'Arcy Thompson
1939–1949	Dr John E. Mackenzie
1949–1959	Dr Douglas Guthrie
1959–1969	Dr Robert Schlapp
1969–1978	Dr Hugh Butler
1978–	Mr Douglas M. Henderson

Portraits, Photographs and Statues

Portraits

A fuller description of the portraits hung in 22, 24 George Street, is given by Dr Douglas Guthrie (*Year Book*, 1960, p. 5)

Bartholomew, John George, sketch portrait by E. A. Walton, 1911.

Brewster, Sir David, by Norman Macbeth, 1869, at the order of the Society.

Brown, Alexander Crum, by E. A. Walton, 1909. Bequeathed by Crum Brown.

Buccleuch, Henry Duke of, by Sir J. Watson Gordon, 1830. Presented by the Duke of Buccleuch, 1840.

Cameron, Hon. Lord, by Alan Sutherland, 1956. Donated by Lady Cameron.

Christison, Sir Robert, Bt, by Sir George Reid, 1875, at the request of the Society.

Davy, Sir Humphry, copy of a painting by Laurence, said to be by James Lonsdale. Purchased by the Society, 1849.

Forbes, James David, by Sir J. Watson Gordon, 1860, at the request of the Society.

Hall, Sir James, Bt, by Sir J. Watson Gordon, 1829. Presented by John Hall.

Kendall, James P., by his daughter, Miss Alice R. Kendall.

Makdougall Brisbane, Sir Thomas, Bt, by Sir J. Watson Gordon, 1848. Subscribed by Fellows.

Murdoch, William, by J. Graham,* *c.* 1809. Presented by the Edinburgh Gas Co. in 1828.

Neill, Patrick, by John Syme. Bequeathed by Miss Anna Neill, 1869.

Ritchie, James, by A. E. Borthwick.

Robison, Professor John, by Sir Henry Raeburn, 1828. Presented by Sir John Robison.

Sang, Edward, by A. R. Moffatt.

Scott, Sir Walter, Bt, by John Graham Gilbert,* 1829, at the request of the Society.

---

* John Graham for a period exhibited under this name, but after marrying a Miss Gilbert, added her name to his and signed himself John Graham Gilbert. We are indebted for this information to Mr. R. E. Hutchinson, Keeper of the Scottish National Portrait Gallery.

Sharpey-Schafer, Sir Edward, by William Walls.

Smith, Sir William Wright, presented by the artist, Stanley Cursiter, R.S.A.

Smyth, Charles Piazzi, by John Faed, R.S.A.

Tait, Peter Guthrie, by Sir George Reid, P.R.S.A. 1892. Presented by subscribers.

Thompson, Sir D'Arcy Wentworth, by David S. Ewart, 1938.

Watt, James, A copy of the original painted by Sir William Beechey, 1801. Presented by James Watt's son.

Photographs and Engravings

See Dr Douglas Guthrie, *Year Book*, 1960, p. 17

Ashworth, James Hartley, Photograph by A. Swan Watson.

Banks, Sir Joseph, Bart, Engraving by F. Cousins from the sculpture by Chantrey.

Beaton, W. J., Photograph by J. Campbell Harper.

Bower, F. O., Photograph.

Campbell, George, 9th Duke of Argyll, From portrait by G. F. Watts.

Chrystal, George, Engraving by C. W. Walton.

Davidson, James Norman, Photograph by Walter Bird.

Ewing, Sir James Alfred, Photograph by A. Swan Watson.

Feather, Norman, Photograph.

Geikie, Sir Archibald, Engraving after the portrait by R. G. Eves.

Geikie, James, Photograph.

Griffith, Sir Richard, Bt, Photograph.

Hirst, Sir Edmund Langley, Photograph.

Horne, John, Photograph by A. Swan Watson.

Huggins, Sir William.

Kelland, Rev. Philip, Reproduction of a picture by William Hole.

Kelvin, Lord, Photograph of a portrait.

Knott, Gilston Cargill, Photograph by A. Swan Watson.

MacCulloch, John, Engraving from a portrait by B. R. Paulkner.

Mackenzie, Henry, Engraving from a portrait by A. Geddes (1822).

MacLagan, Sir Douglas, Photograph of a portrait.

Milne-Holme, David, Lithograph by H. Rhodes.

Moncreiff, Lord, Engraving by F. Schenck after Otto Leyde.

Murray, Sir John.

Napier, John, Photograph of a portrait.

Rayleigh, Lord, Engraving from portrait by Sir George Reid.

Richey, James E., Photograph by Yerbury.

Robertson, Rev William, Engraving by J. Dixon from portrait by Sir Joshua Reynolds.

Sampson, R. A. Photograph by Drummond Young

Smith, R. A., Photograph by his son.

Stephenson, Robert, Engraving from a portrait by John Lucas.

Stevenson, Thomas, Photograph of a portrait.

Stewart, George A., Photograph by John Moffat.

Telford, Thomas (1757–1834), Engraving by H. Macbeth-Raeburn, R.A. of portrait by Sir Henry Raeburn.

Thomson, J. J., Photograph from an oil painting by Fiddes Watt.

Turner, William, Photograph from portrait by Sir James Guthrie.

Yonge, Sir Maurice, Photograph.

Busts and Statues

See Douglas Guthrie, *Year Book*, 1959–60, p. 16

Berzelius, Jons Jakob, Plaster bust by F. Tieck, 1822.

Cuvier, Leopold C. F. D., Large plaster bust by David d'Angers.

Gordon, James, Plaster bust by D. W. Stevenson, R.S.A.

Hume, David, Bronze statuette presented by the sculptor Pittendrigh Macgillivray, R.S.A. It is the original of a full-sized statue in the National Gallery of Scotland.

Hutton, James, Plaster bust.

Kelvin, Lord, Marble bust by A. M'F. Shannan, A.R.S.A. Presented by Lady Kelvin.

Makdougall Brisbane, Sir Thomas, Plaster bust.

Meadowbank, Lord, Plaster bust by Sir George Mackenzie (c. 1820).

Moncreiff, Rev. Sir Henry Wellwood, Bt, Plaster bust by Samuel Joseph, R.S.A.

Murchison, Sir Roderick Impey, Marble bust by H. Weekes, R.A. (1871).

Napier, John, Plaster bust.

Playfair, Professor John, Plaster bust by Sir Francis Chantrey.

Scott, Sir Walter, Plaster bust.

Sinclair, Sir John, Small stucco statuette.

Whittaker, Sir Edmund, Bronze portrait head by Benno Schotz. Subscribed by Fellows.

Name Index

Subject Index

List of Sponsors

The Society wishes to record its gratitude for the considerable financial help provided by the following Edinburgh organisations:

The John M. Archer Charitable Trust
George Boyd & Co. Ltd
The British Linen Bank Ltd
C. & J. Brown of Newington
Caledonian Packaging Ltd
Chemco Equipment Finance Ltd
Citibank N.A.
R. Drysdale & Co. Ltd
Dunedin Management Advisory Services
Ethicon Ltd
Featherhall Press Ltd
Garland & Roger
James Grant (East) PLC
James Gray & Son
Hall Advertising Ltd
Herrald Antiques
Hong Kong & Shanghai Banking Corporation
I.C.I. PLC
Industrial & Commercial Finance Corp. Ltd
Jenners Ltd
Kinloch Anderson Ltd
Kennerty Farm Dairies Ltd
Laidlaw, Drew & Co. Ltd
Lloyds and Scottish Trust Ltd
Longman Group Ltd
Lorimer & Beetham
Lothian Chemical Co. Ltd
MacGregor & Co. (Glass & China) Ltd
Martin & Frost
John Millar & Sons
James Miller & Partners Ltd
The Sir James Miller Edinburgh Trust
National Westminster Bank Ltd
North British Cold Storage & Ice Co. Ltd
Office Cleaning Services (Scotland) Ltd
P.A. Management Consultants Ltd
Martin Paterson Associates Ltd
Pillans & Wilson Ltd
Pullman Pans Ltd
Rae MacIntosh (Music) Ltd
Rankins' Fruit Markets Ltd
Reed Corrugated Cases Ltd
R. & S. Robertson Ltd
Christian Salvesen Ltd
Scobie & McIntosh Ltd
Scotia Frozen Foods Ltd
James Scott & Co. (Electrical Engineers) Ltd
Sculthorps Ltd

Sibbald Travel
Geo. Stewart & Co. Ltd
William Thyne Ltd
U. B. Restaurants Ltd
United Wire Group PLC

Vickers Marine Engineering Division
George Waterston & Sons Ltd
Alexander Wilkie Ltd
T. G. Willis & Co. Ltd